History Alive!®

The Ancient World

Interactive Student Notebook

Teachers' Curriculum Institute

Managing Editor: Laura Alavosus
Developmental Editor: John Bergez
Production Editor: Mali Apple
Editorial Assistant: Anna Embree
Art Director: Tim Stephenson
Production Manager: Lynn Sanchez
Senior Graphic Designer: Christy Uyeno
Graphic Designers: Katy Haun, Paul Rebello, Don Taka
Photo Editor: Lindsay Kefauver
Audio Director: Katy Haun
Operations Manager: Ellen Mapstone

Teachers' Curriculum Institute
P.O. Box 50996
Palo Alto, CA 94303

ISBN13: 978-1-58371-358-7 ISBN10: 1-58371-358-1
21 -DH- 14 13

Manufactured by Hess Print Solutions, Woodstock, IL, United States of America, November 2013, Job #253285

Program Directors

Bert Bower

Jim Lobdell

Author

Wendy Frey

Contributing Writers

John Bergez

Amy Joseph

Curriculum Developers

Joyce Bartky

Terry Coburn

Anne Maloney

Steve Seely

Kelly Shafsky

Reading Specialist

Kate Kinsella, Ed.D
Reading and TESOL Specialist
Department of Secondary Education
College of Education
San Francisco State University
San Francisco, California

Teacher Consultants

Melissa Aubuchon
Indian Trail Middle School
Plainfield School District 202
Plainfield, Illinois

Anthony Braxton
Cruickshank Middle School
Merced City School District
Merced, California

Amy George
Weston Middle School
Weston Public Schools
Weston, Massachusetts

Randi Gibson
Stanford Middle School
Long Beach Unified School District
Long Beach, California

Lisa Macurak
New Windsor Middle School
Carroll County Schools
New Windsor, Maryland

Sherry Owens
Lubbock Independent School District
Lubbock, Texas

Scholars

Dr. Anthony Bulloch
Professor of Classics
University of California
Berkeley, California

Dr. Mark W. Chavalas
Department of History
University of Wisconsin
La Crosse, Wisconsin

Dr. Eun Mi Cho
Department of Special Education
California State University
Sacramento, California

Dr. Bruce Grelle
Department of Religious Studies
Director, Religion and Public Education Resource Center
California State University
Chico, California

Dr. David N. Keightley
Professor Emeritus of History
University of California
Berkeley, California

Dr. Brij Khare
Professor Emeritus
California State University
San Bernardino, California

Dr. Gary Miles
Professor Emeritus of History
Cowell College
University of California
Santa Cruz, California

Dr. Daniel Veidlinger
Department of Religious Studies
California State University
Chico, California

Dr. Jed Wyrick
Department of Religious Studies
California State University
Chico, California

Dr. Joel Zimbelman
Chair, Department of Religious Studies
California State University
Chico, California

Assessment Consultants

Denny Chandler
Curriculum and Assessment Specialist
Cold Spring, Kentucky

Julie Weiss
Curriculum and Assessment Specialist
Elliot, Maine

Music Consultant

Melanie T. Pinkert, Ethnomusicologist
Bethesda, Maryland

Geography Specialist

Mapping Specialists
Madison, Wisconsin

Internet Consultant

Amy George
Weston, Massachusetts

Diverse Needs Consultants

Erin Fry
Glendora, California

Colleen Guccione
Naperville, Illinois

Contents

Unit 1

Early Humans and the Rise of Civilization

Unit 2

Ancient Egypt and the Near East

Unit 3

Ancient India

Unit 4

Ancient China

Unit 5

Ancient Greece

Unit 6

Ancient Rome

UNIT 1

Early Humans and the Rise of Civilization

GEOGRAPHY CHALLENGE 1

To complete each Geography Challenge card, answer the questions in complete sentences.
Label the map on the opposite page as directed. Questions 5–8 are on page 6.

Question 1 ______________________________

____

Question 2 ______________________________

____

Question 3 ______________________________

____

Question 4 ______________________________

____

GEOGRAPHY CHALLENGE 1

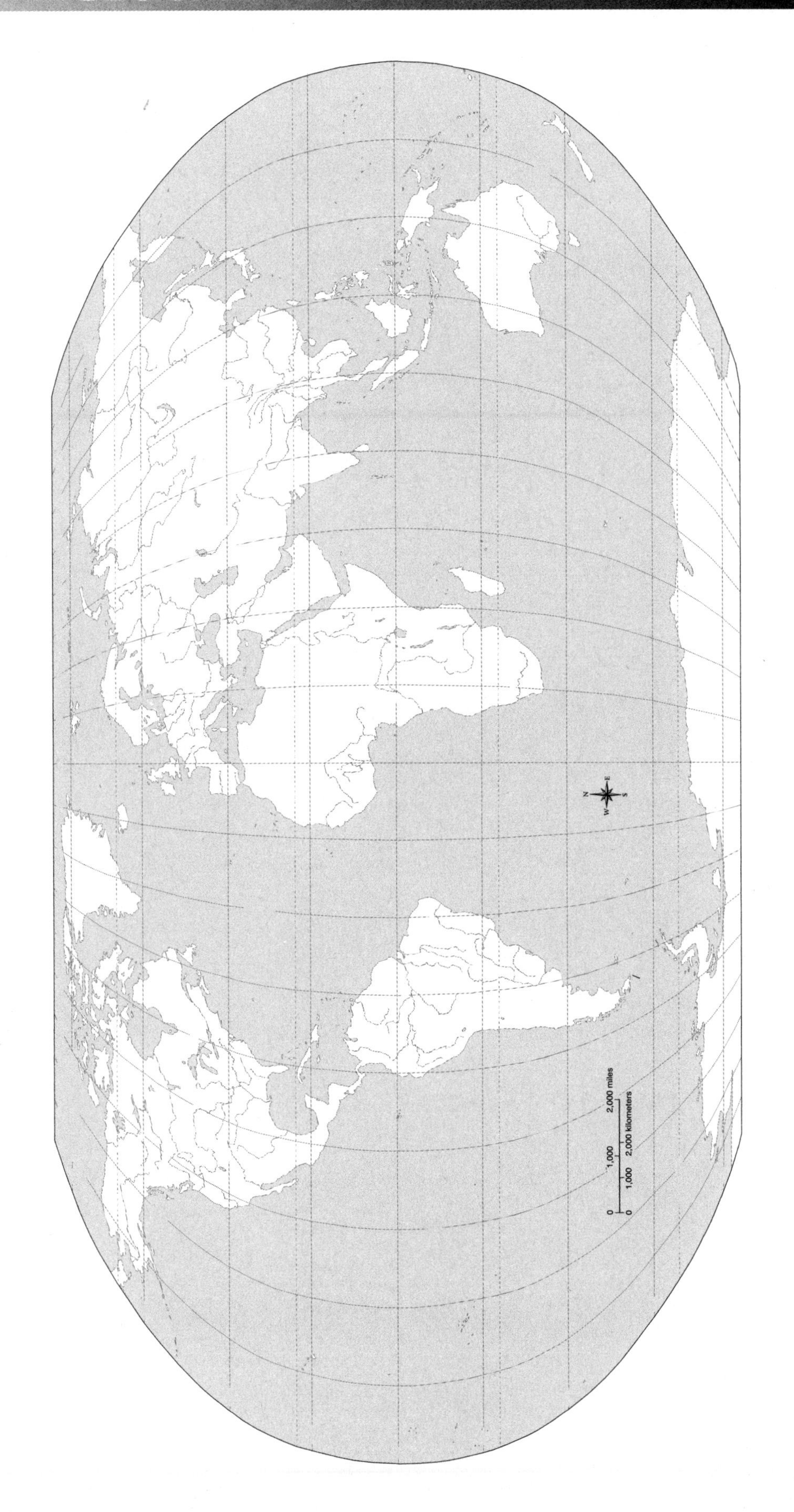

GEOGRAPHY CHALLENGE 1

To complete each Geography Challenge card, answer the questions in complete sentences. Label the map on the opposite page as directed. Questions 1–4 are on page 4.

Question 5 ____________________

____

Question 6 ____________________

____

Question 7 ____________________

____

Question 8 ____________________

____

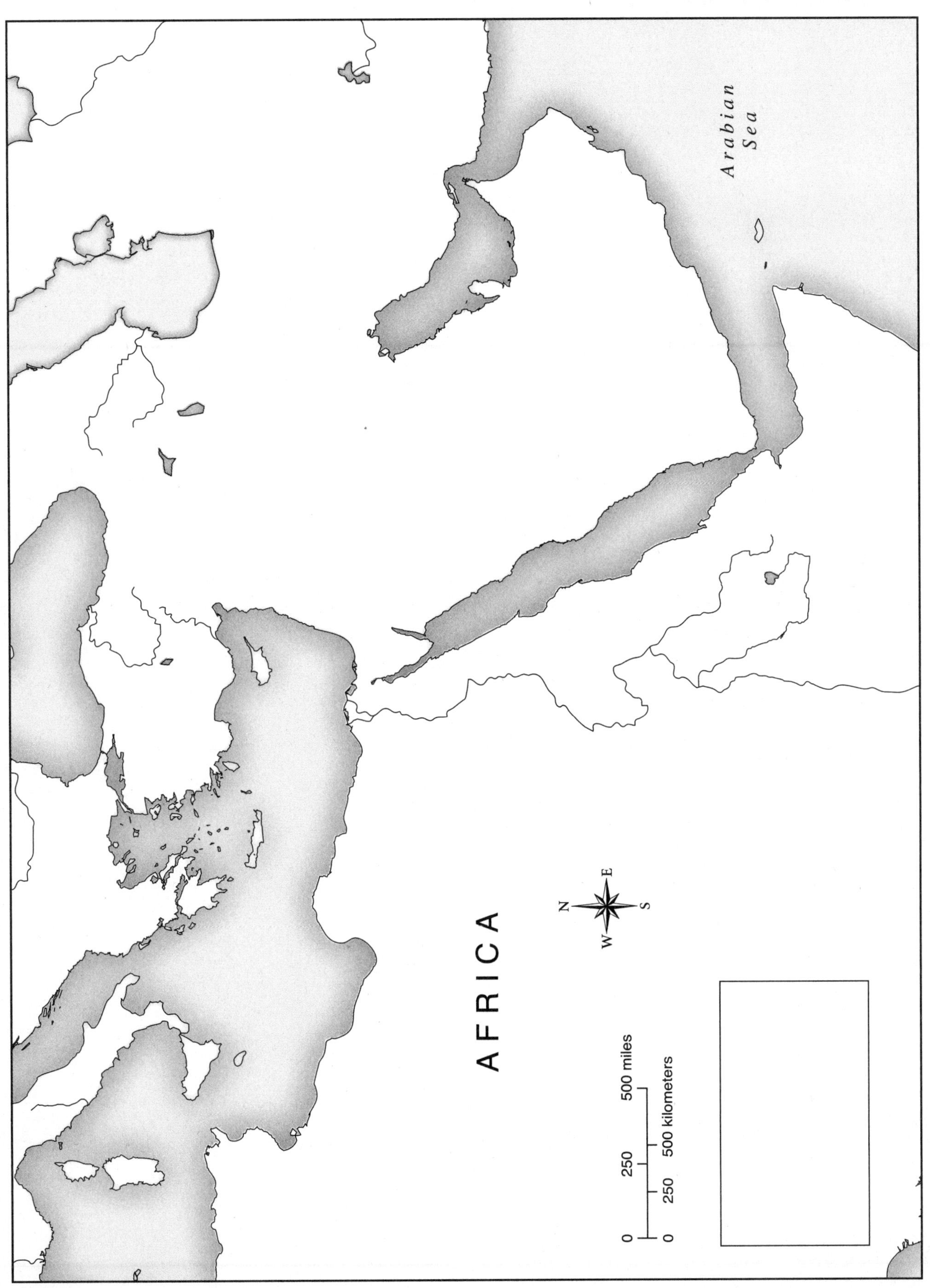
Arabian Sea
AFRICA
N
E
S
W
0 250 500 miles
0 250 500 kilometers

PREVIEW 1

In the space below, quickly sketch one object you currently own that you think someone might find 20,000 years from now.

Pretend you are a social scientist living 20,000 years from now. You have just discovered the object above. What might the object tell you about the person who left it behind? Write your thoughts in a short paragraph below.

READING NOTES 1

In this activity, you will try to discover what six cave artifacts reveal about early humans. Carefully examine each photograph from the cave. Match it to one of these images. Complete that section of the Reading Notes.

Transparency 1: Cave Painting of a Human

Find evidence: Label three details in the image that may offer clues about why the artist created this painting.

Our hypothesis: We think the artist created this because...

Read Section 1.4. Why do social scientists think this painting was created?

Placard 1A: Cave Painting of Animals

Find evidence: Label two details in the image that may offer clues about why the artist created this painting.

Our hypothesis: We think the artist created this because...

Read Section 1.5. Why do social scientists think this painting was created?

Placard 1B: Cave Painting of Shapes and Handprints

Find evidence: Label three details in the image that may offer clues about why the artist created this painting.

Our hypothesis: We think the artist created this because...

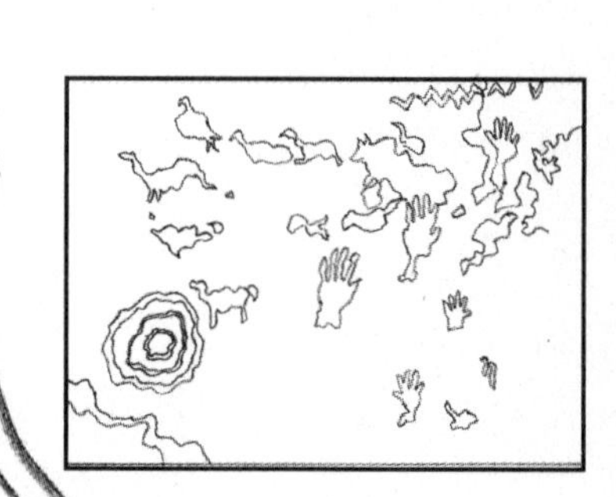

Read Section 1.6. Why do social scientists think this painting was created?

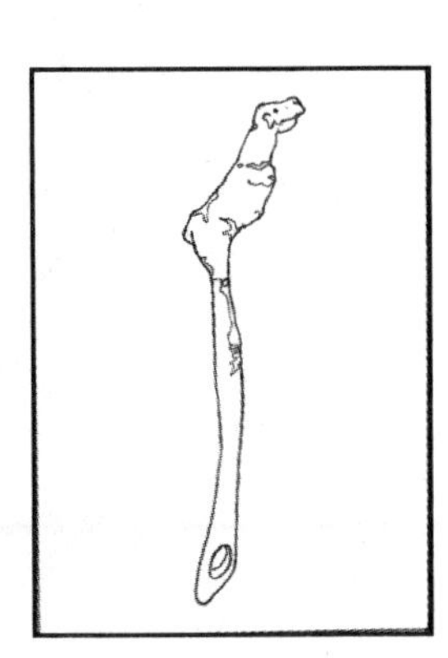

Placard 1C: Spear Thrower

Find evidence: Label two details in the image that may offer clues about why the artist created this tool.

Our hypothesis: We think the artist created this because...

Read Section 1.7. Why do social scientists think this tool was created?

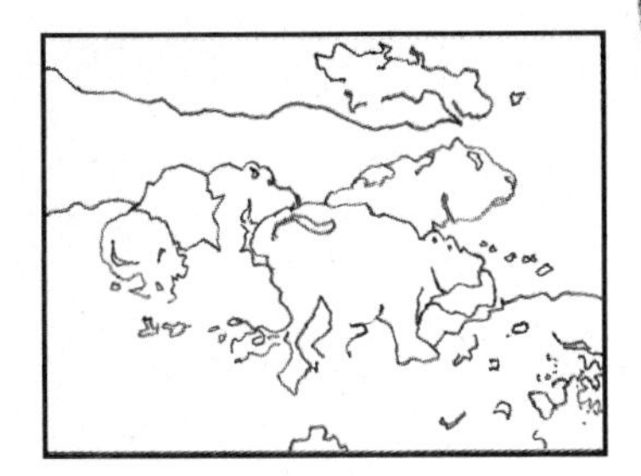

Placard 1D: Clay Sculptures

Find evidence: Label two details in the image that may offer clues about why the artist created these sculptures.

Our hypothesis: We think the artist created these because...

Read Section 1.8. Why do social scientists think these sculptures were created?

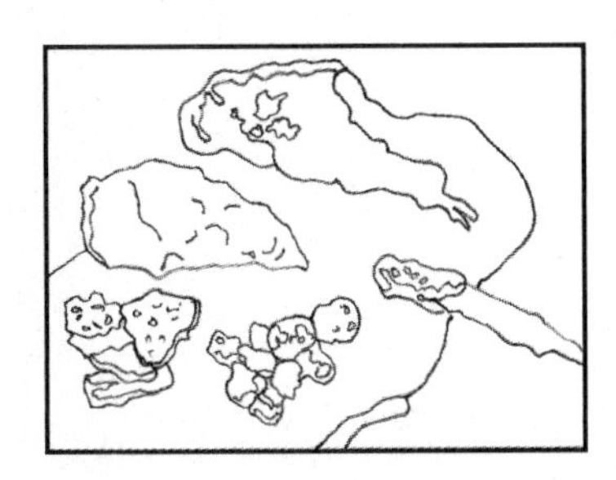

Placard 1E: Cave Art Tools

Find evidence: Label three details in the image that may offer clues about why the artist created these tools.

Our hypothesis: We think the artist used these tools to...

Read Section 1.9. What do social scientists think these tools were used for?

PROCESSING 1

Create a "cave painting" that represents the most important aspects of your life. Follow these guidelines:

- Use a sheet of butcher or poster paper, approximately 18 by 24 inches.
- Use charcoal, red-brown paint, or markings made with natural materials.
- Show at least five different objects in your painting.

PREVIEW 2

Think of a simple problem or challenge that you face almost every day. For example, you may have trouble getting out of bed in the morning to get ready for school.

Next, think of a tool or machine that would help solve your problem. For example, a robot that automatically lifts you out of bed and carries you to the bathroom might solve the problem above.

In the space below, draw a picture of your tool or machine. Create a name for it. Under your drawing, write one or two sentences explaining how your invention will make your life better.

READING NOTES 2

Sections 2.2 and 2.3

1. Write the name of this hominid:

_ _

2. Color the rectangle that matches the time period in which this hominid lived.

4 million years B.C.E.	3 million years B.C.E.	2 million years B.C.E.	1 million years B.C.E.	Today

3. Color or draw and label the key capabilities of this hominid.

4. Explain why these capabilities were important.

Sections 2.4 and 2.5

1. Write the name of this hominid:

_ _ _ _   _ _ _ _ _ _ _ _ _ _

2. Color the rectangle that matches the time period in which this hominid lived.

4 million years B.C.E.	3 million years B.C.E.	2 million years B.C.E.	1 million years B.C.E.	Today

3. Color or draw and label the key capabilities of this hominid.

4. Explain why these capabilities were important.

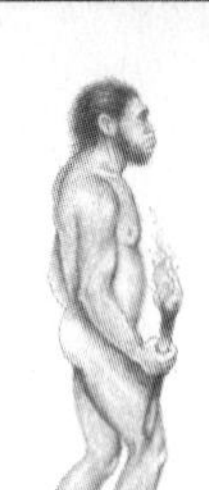

Sections 2.6 and 2.7

1. Write the name of this hominid:

_ _ _ _ _ _ _ _ _ _ _ _ _

2. Color the rectangle that matches the time period in which this hominid lived.

4 million years B.C.E.	3 million years B.C.E.	2 million years B.C.E.	1 million years B.C.E.	Today

3. Color or draw and label the key capabilities of this hominid.

4. Explain why these capabilities were important.

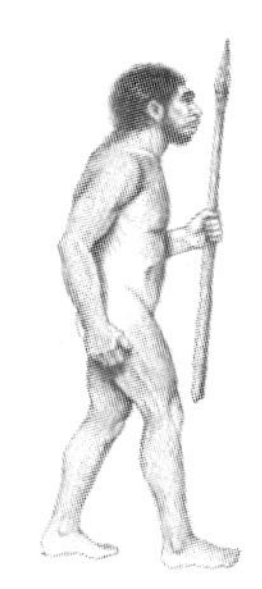

Sections 2.8 and 2.9

1. Write the name of this hominid:

_ _

2. Color the rectangle that matches the time period in which this hominid lived.

4 million years B.C.E. | 3 million years B.C.E. | 2 million years B.C.E. | 1 million years B.C.E. | Today

3. Color or draw and label the key capabilities of this hominid.

4. Explain why these capabilities were important.

READING NOTES 2

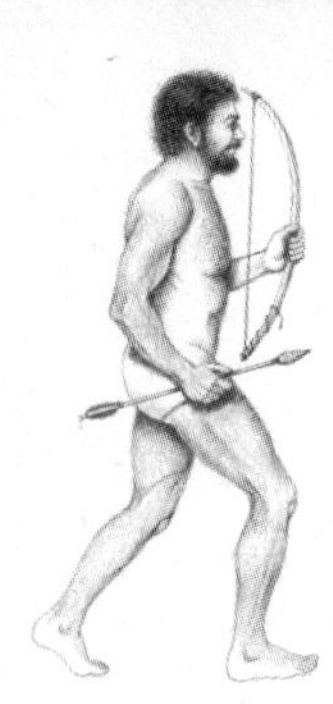

Sections 2.10 and 2.11

1. Write the name of this hominid:

____ _________ _________

2. Color the rectangle that matches the time period in which this hominid lived.

4 million years B.C.E.	3 million years B.C.E.	2 million years B.C.E.	1 million years B.C.E.	Today

3. Color or draw and label the key capabilities of this hominid.

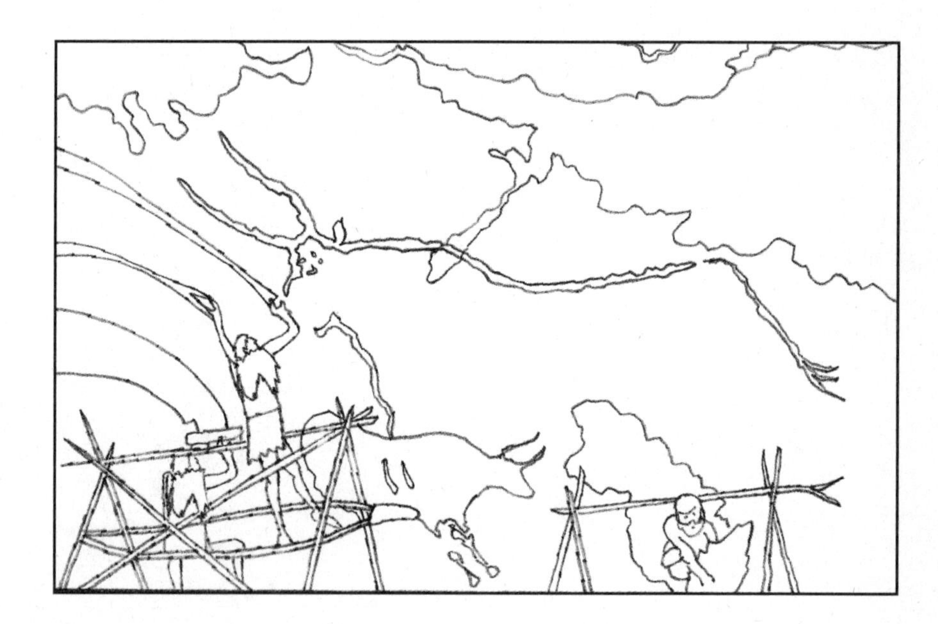

4. Explain why these capabilities were important.

PROCESSING 2

Create a "superhero" poster below for one of the hominids you learned about in this chapter. The poster should focus on the abilities of the hominid you select. Your poster needs to include

- the name of your hominid.
- information on where and when your hominid lived.
- a drawing of your hominid.
- a list of your hominid's important abilities.
- any other creative ideas to make the poster more realistic.

PREVIEW 3

In the space below, create a cartoon that shows one important way life has changed for people since the invention of one of these items:

computer　　　　airplane　　　　CD player

In your cartoon, do the following:

- Complete the sentences to explain what life was like before and after the invention of the item you chose.
- Use simple drawings to show what the people in the cartoon are thinking or saying.

<table>
<tr><td colspan="2">In the past…</td></tr>
<tr><td>But today…</td><td>This change is important because…</td></tr>
</table>

READING NOTES 3

After reading Section 3.3, complete the sentence and fill in the speech bubbles for Neolithic Nel. One example is done for you.

3.3 Creating a Stable Food Supply

In Paleolithic times, the food supply…

What are two important facts about the food supply in the Neolithic Age? Write your answers in the speech bubbles below.

Why are these facts important? Write your answer in the speech bubble below.

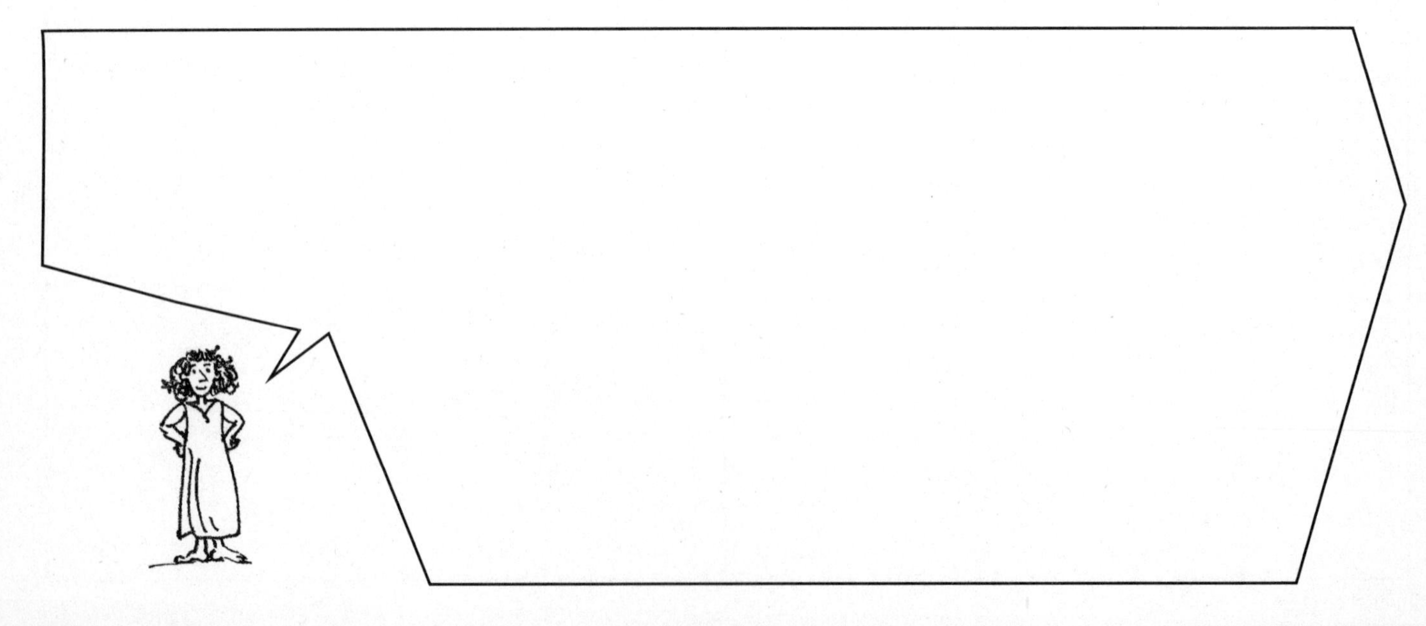

After reading Section 3.4, complete the sentence and fill in the speech bubbles for Neolithic Nick.

3.4 Making Permanent Shelters

In Paleolithic times, shelter…

What are two important facts about shelter in the Neolithic Age? Write your answers in the speech bubbles below.

Why are these facts important? Write your answer in the speech bubble below.

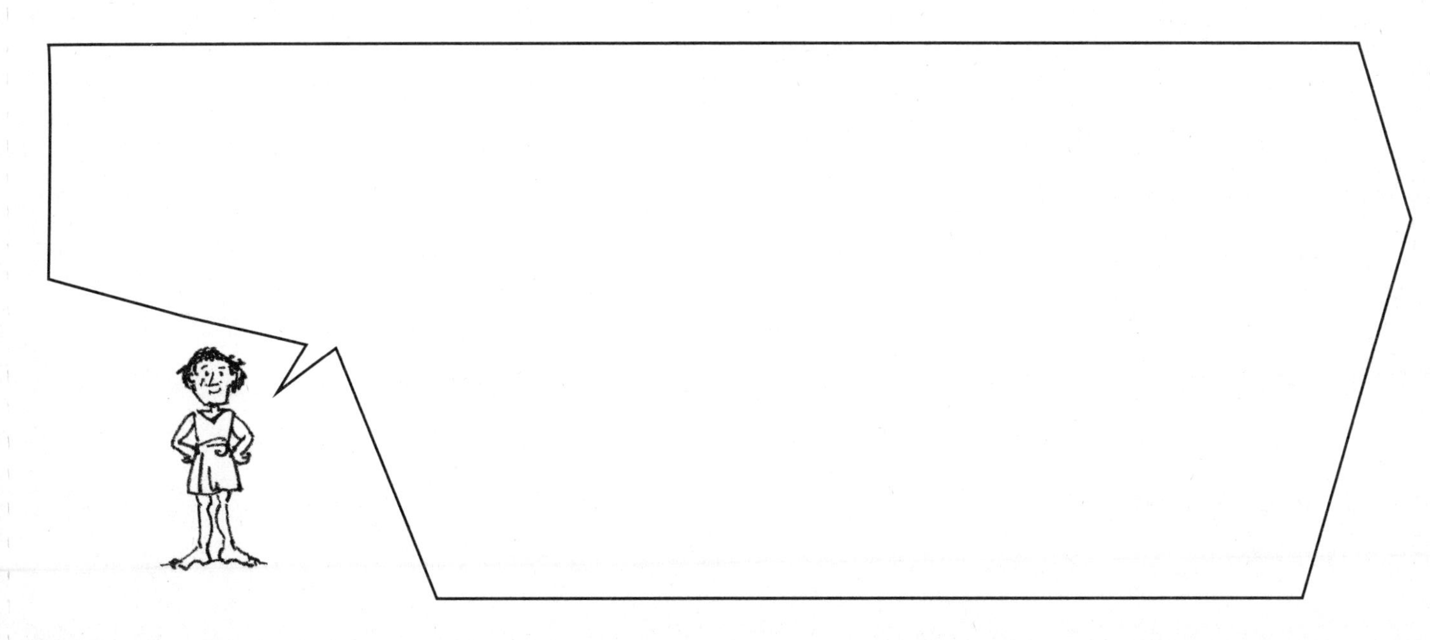

READING NOTES 3

After reading Section 3.5, complete the sentence and fill in the speech bubbles for Neolithic Nel.

3.5 Establishing Communities

In Paleolithic times, communities…

What are two important facts about communities in the Neolithic Age?

Why are these facts important?

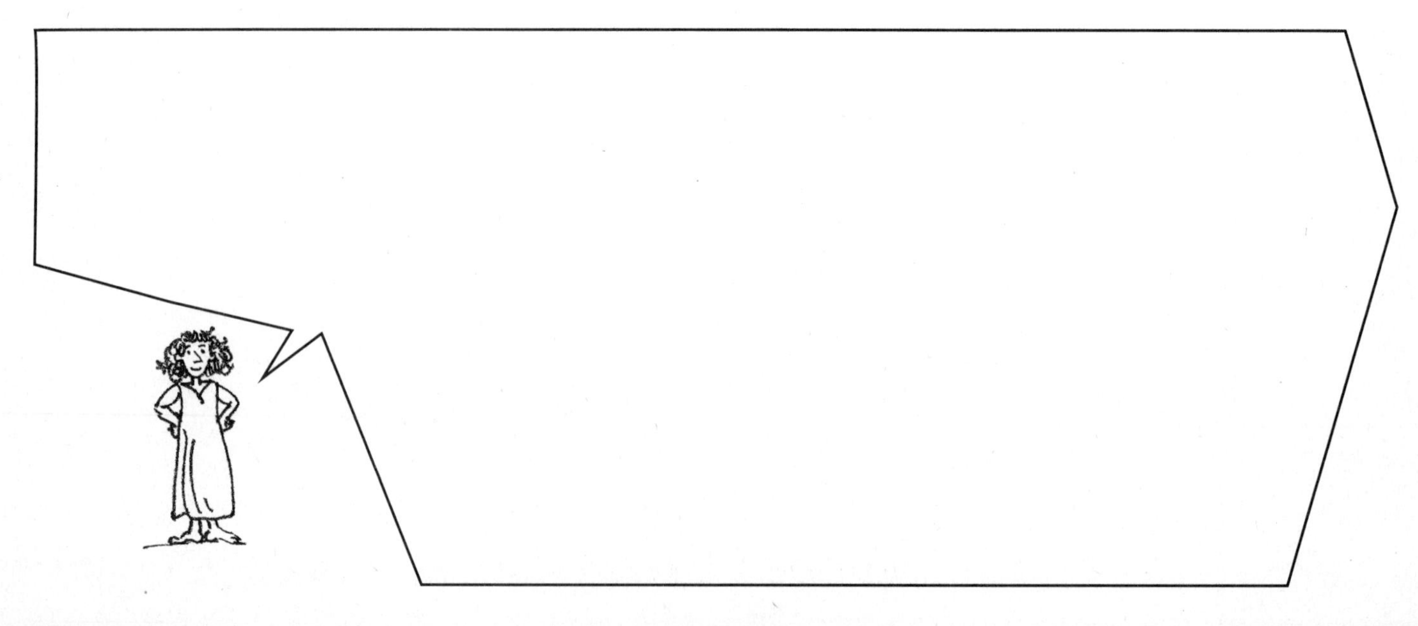

After reading Section 3.6, complete the sentence and fill in the speech bubbles for Neolithic Nick.

3.6 Developing New Jobs

In Paleolithic times, jobs…

What are two important facts about jobs in the Neolithic Age?

Why are these facts important?

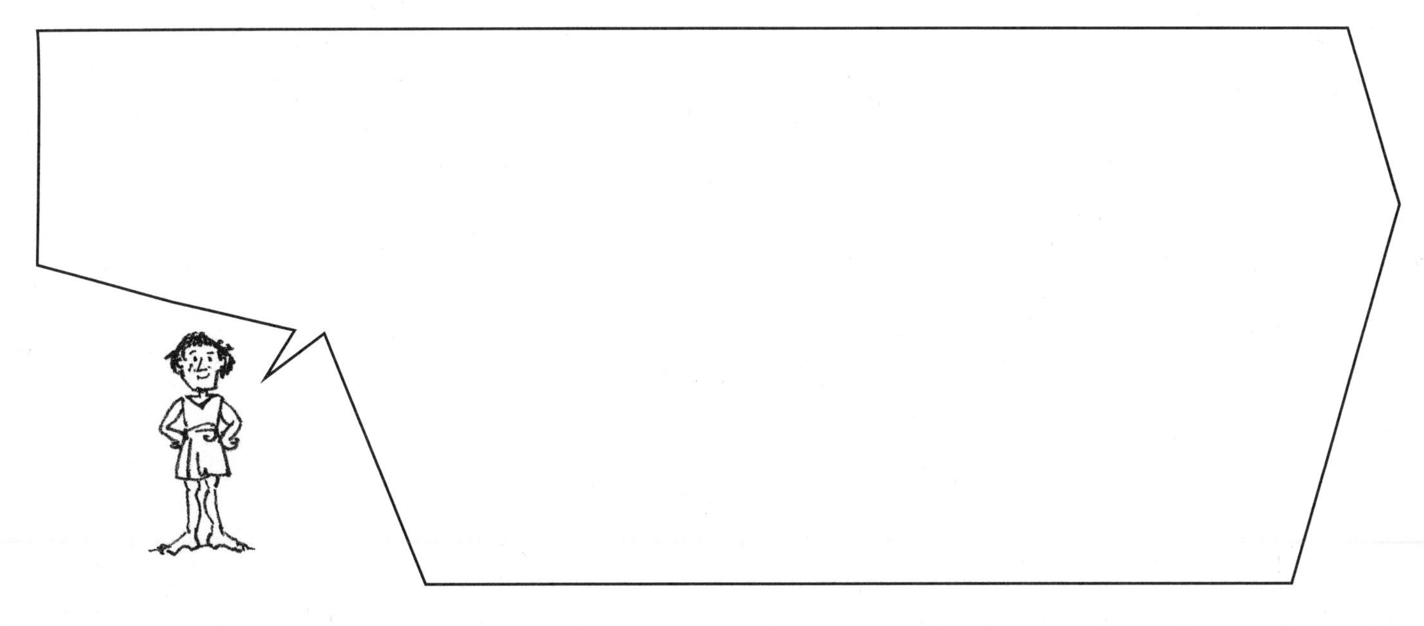

READING NOTES 3

After reading Section 3.7, complete the sentence and fill in the speech bubbles for Neolithic Nel.

3.7 Beginning to Trade

In Paleolithic times, trade…

What are two important facts about trade in the Neolithic Age?

Why are these facts important?

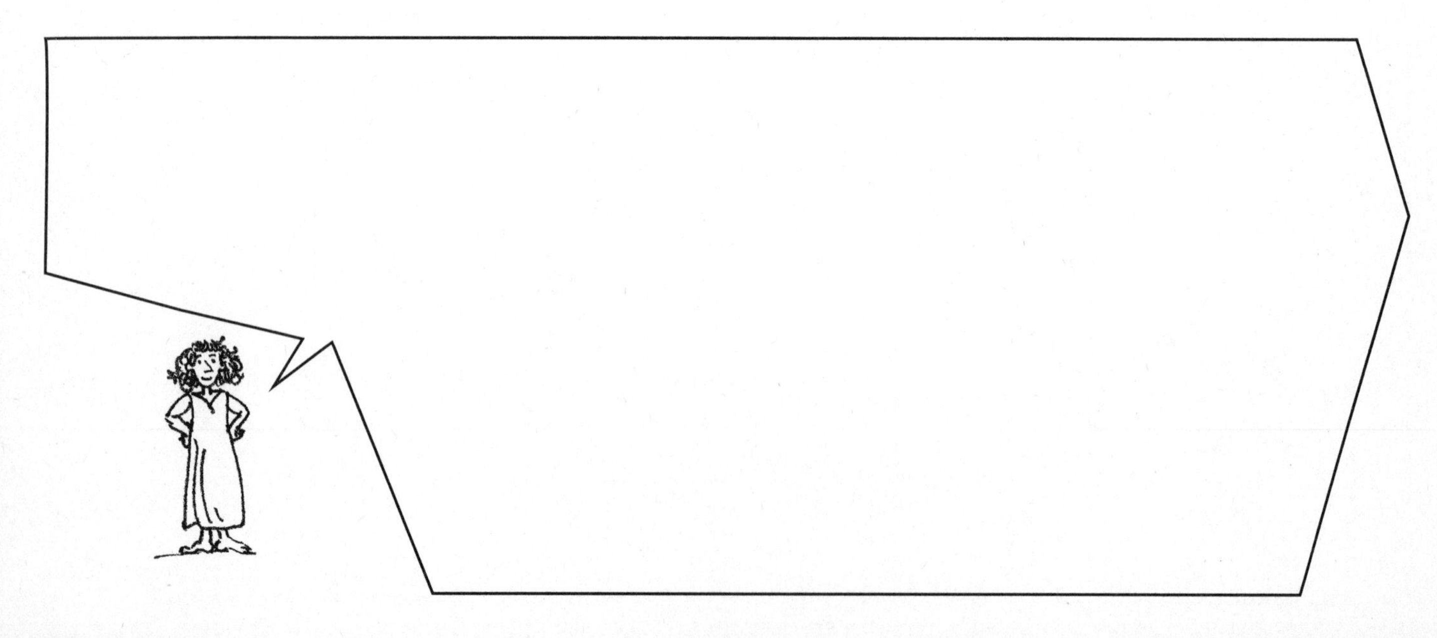

PREVIEW 4

Think of a recent problem or challenge that you, your family, or your school faced, and what you did to solve it.

In the flowchart below, draw a simple illustration of the challenge in the "Problem" box. Also write a one- or two-sentence summary of the problem in that box.

In the "Solution" box, draw a simple illustration of how you solved the problem. Also write one or two sentences describing the solution.

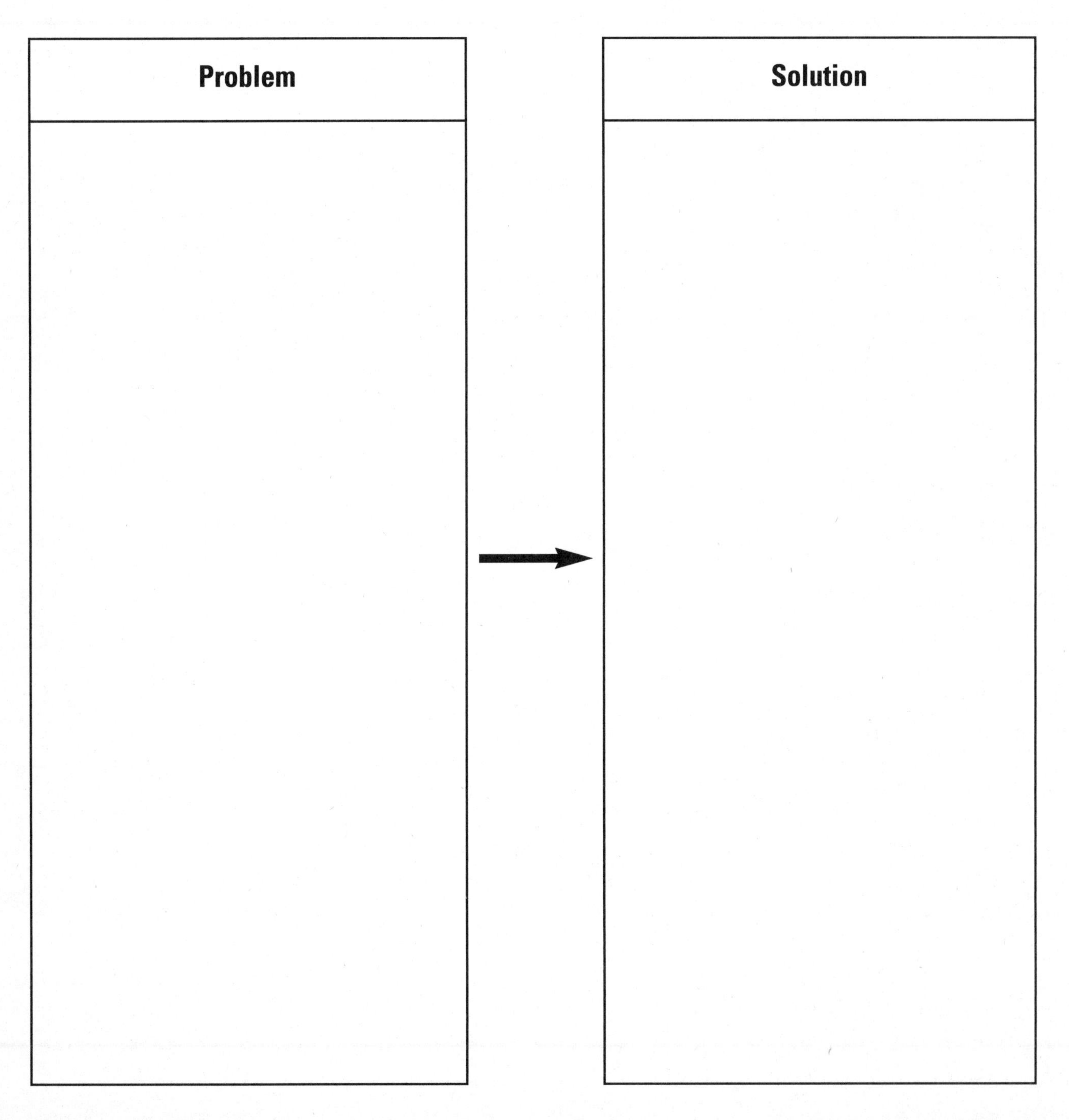

READING NOTES 4

After reading each section in your book, fill in the "Problem" and "Solution" boxes in the flowchart. In each box, create a simple drawing to illustrate the problem or solution (two drawings are done for you). Also write a one- or two-sentence summary of the problem or solution in the box.

4.3 Food Shortages in the Hills

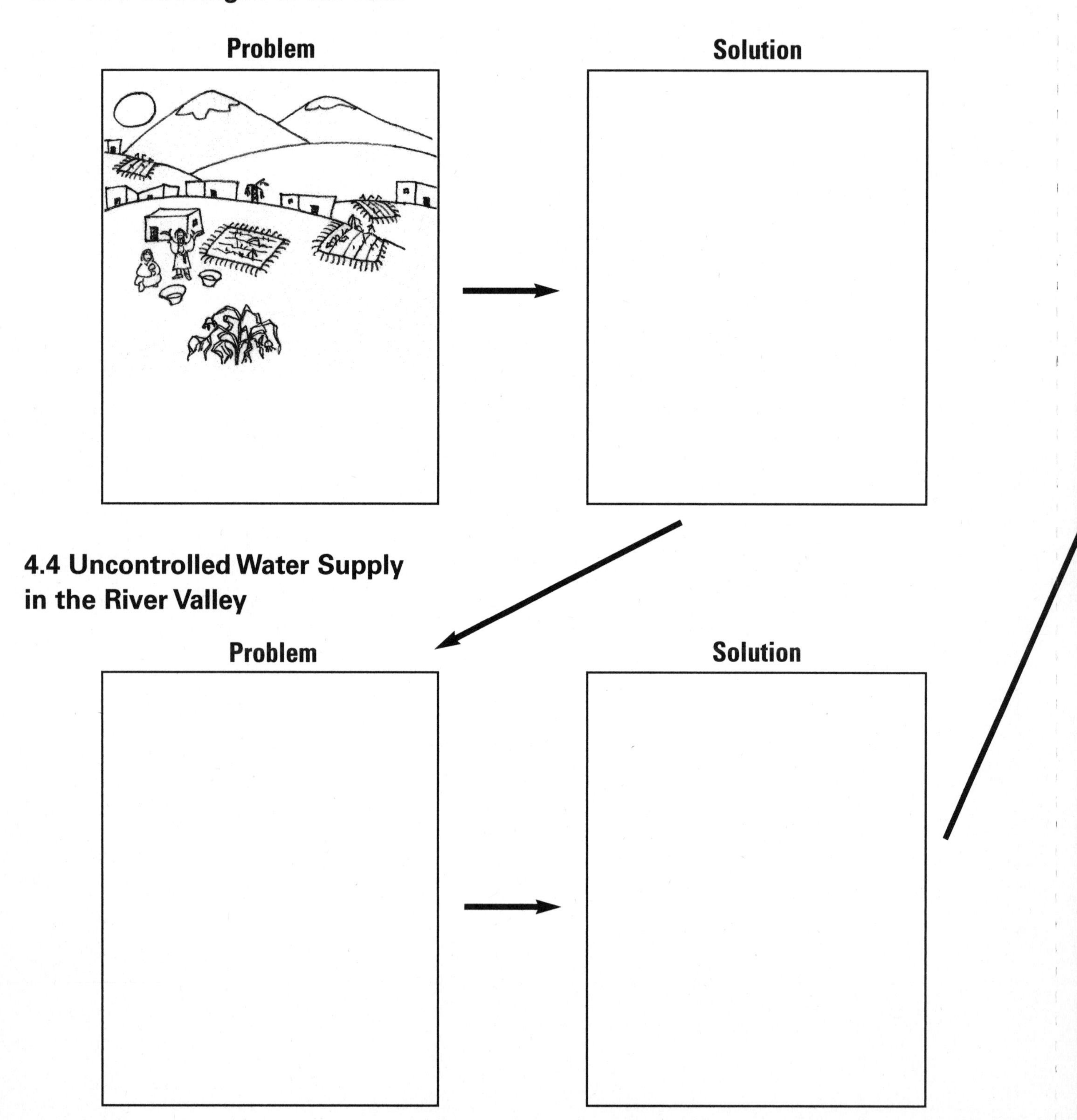

4.4 Uncontrolled Water Supply in the River Valley

READING NOTES 4

4.5 Difficulties in Building and Maintaining a Complex Irrigation System

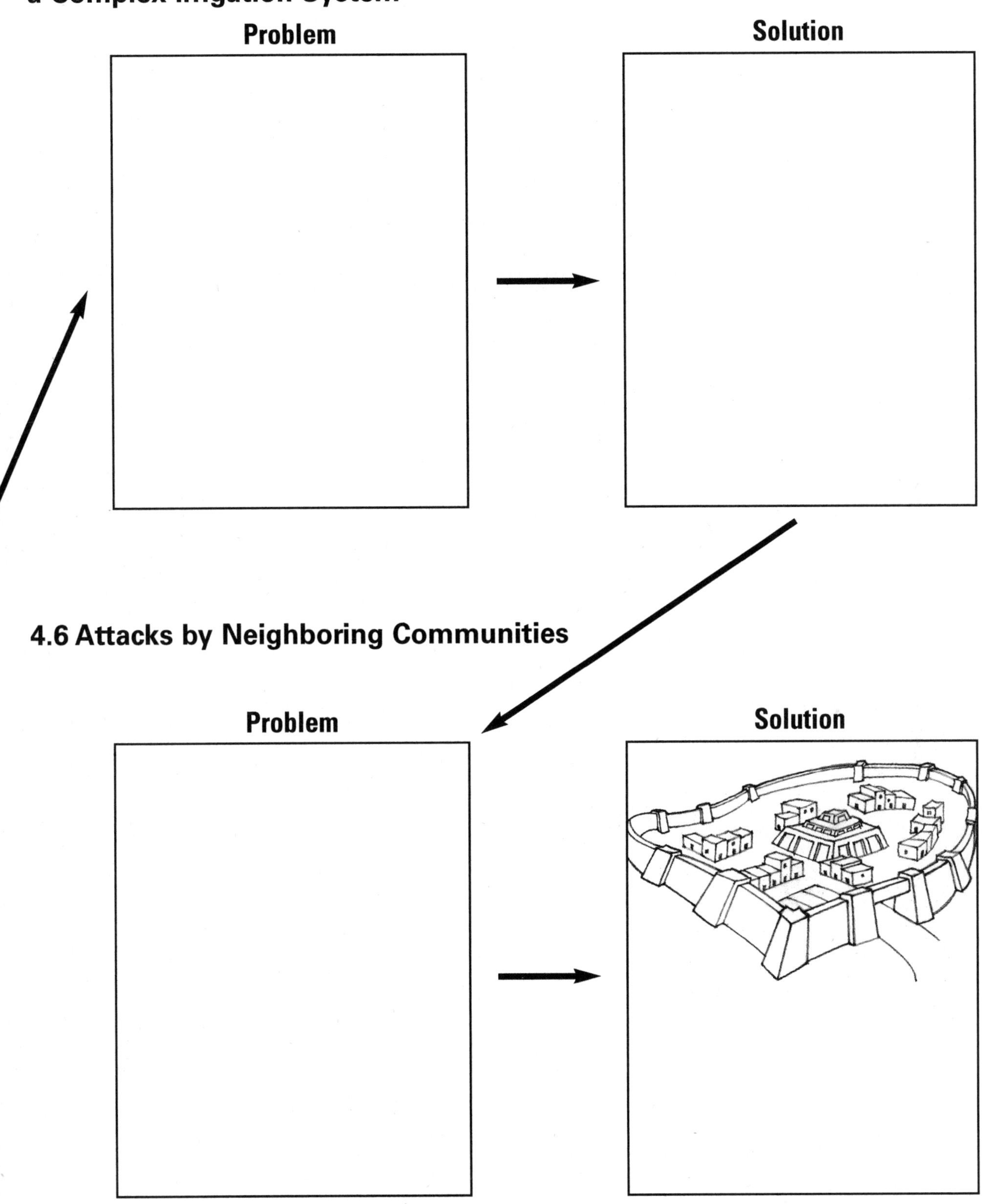

PROCESSING 4

In the space below, create a real-estate advertisement to encourage people to move to one of the Sumerian city-states. Make sure your advertisement includes these things:

- An appropriate and clever title for the advertisement, to catch the reader's eye. Be sure it includes the words *Sumerian city-states.*
- At least three illustrations representing the ideas Sumerians came up with to solve to key problems.
- A brief caption for each visual that describes the solution and explains how or why it helps make a Sumerian city-state a desirable place to live.

PREVIEW 5

Scientists sometimes describe a society or group of humans as "highly civilized." What do you think this means?

Fill in the empty spokes of the diagram below with words that describe characteristics of a society that is highly civilized. For each spoke, draw and label a simple example of that description. One spoke is completed for you.

READING NOTES 5

After reading one section of Chapter 5 in *History Alive! The Ancient World* and analyzing all the artifacts from ancient Sumer, follow these steps:

1. Find the oval in the diagrams on this and the following three pages that corresponds to the section you read.
2. In the space around that oval, make a simple drawing of *each artifact* you analyzed that you think is an example of that characteristic of civilization.
3. Next to each drawing, complete this sentence: *(Name of artifact) relates to this characteristic of civilization because...*
4. Complete the spoke diagram by connecting each drawing to the oval with a line.

5.3
Stable Food Supply

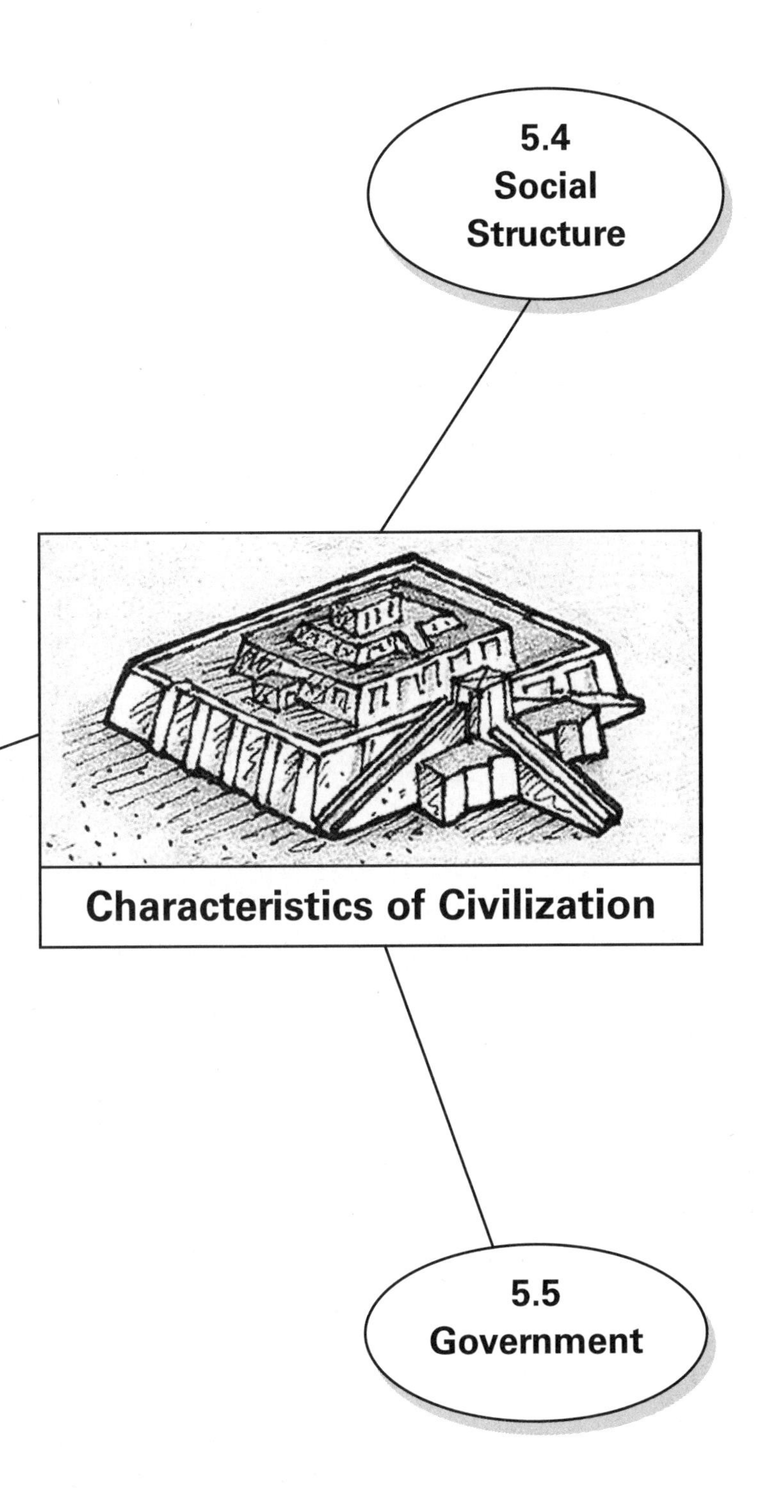

5.4
Social
Structure
Characteristics of Civilization
5.5
Government

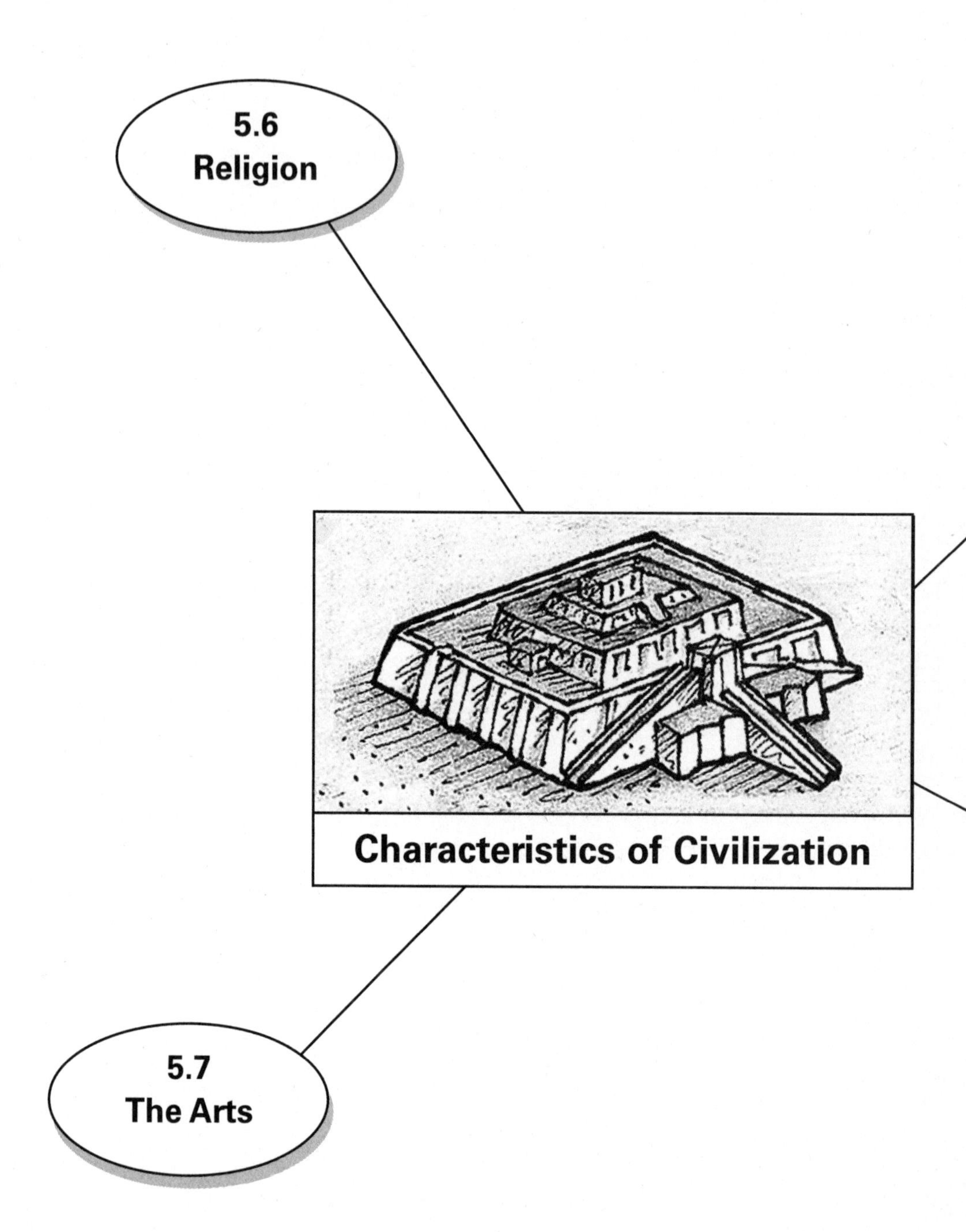
5.6
Religion
Characteristics of Civilization
5.7
The Arts

5.8
Technology

5.9
Writing

PROCESSING 5

Complete the spoke diagram below by drawing or finding pictures of modern items that are examples of each characteristic of civilization. For each picture, follow these steps:

1. Glue or draw the picture next to the characteristic to which you think it is related.
2. Complete this sentence: *(Name of artifact) relates to this characteristic of civilization because….*
3. Draw a line connecting the picture to the oval.

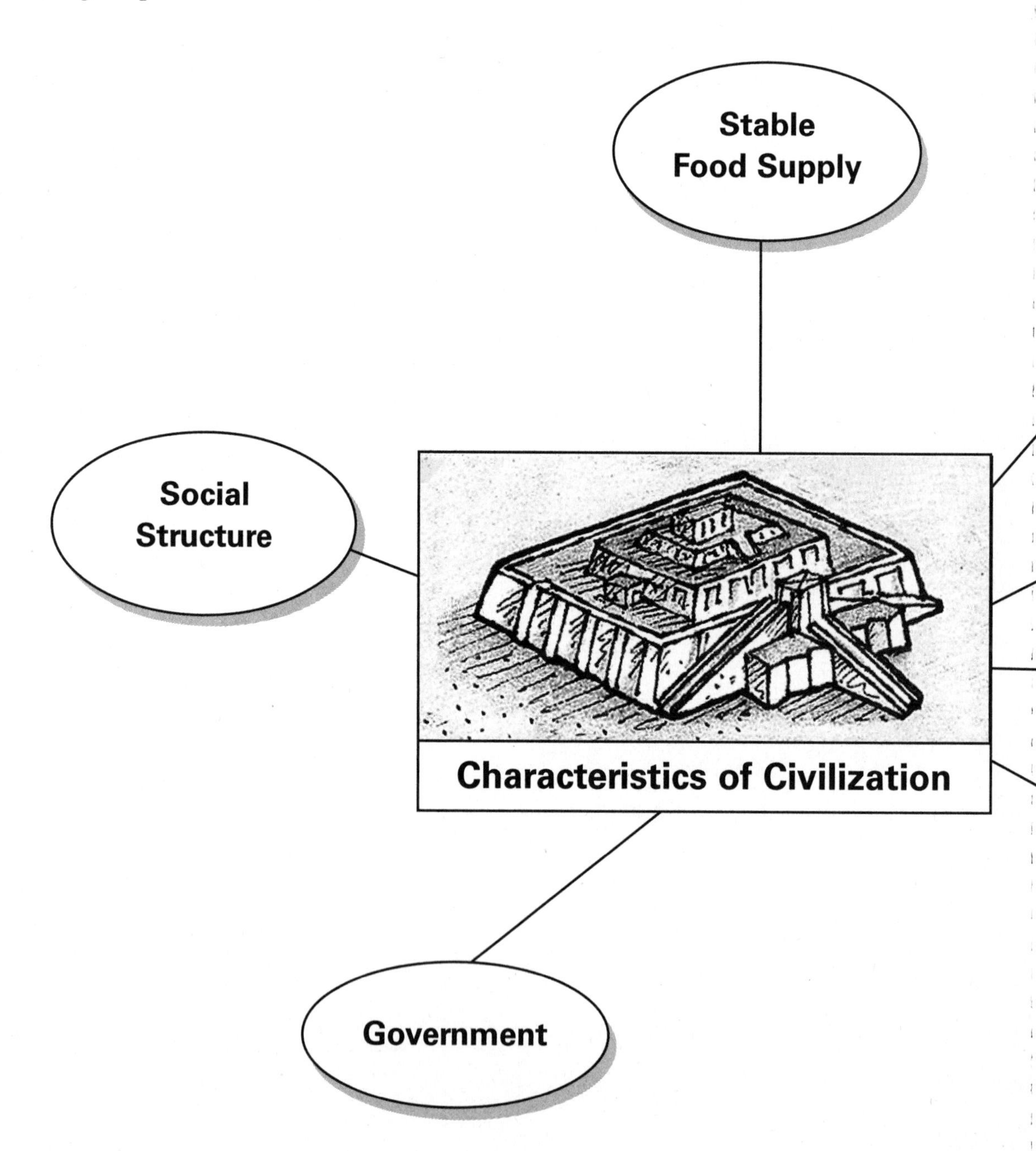

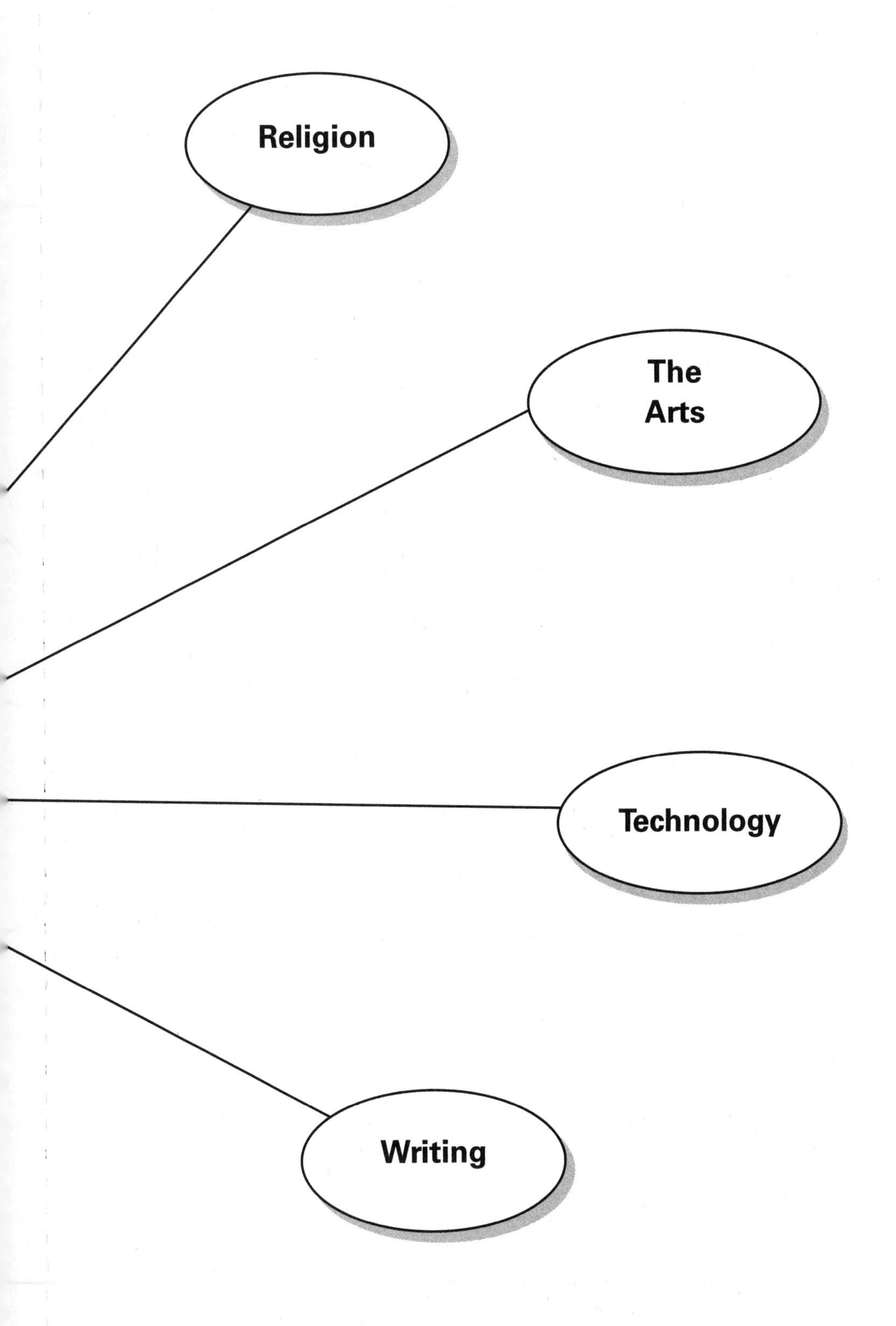
Religion
The
Arts
Technology
Writing

In ancient Mesopotamia, rulers recorded their most important achievements on steles. A *stele* is a stone slab on which an illustration or inscription has been carved.

Complete the two steles below to celebrate two of your most important personal achievements. Draw pictures or find photographs of images or symbols to represent each achievement.

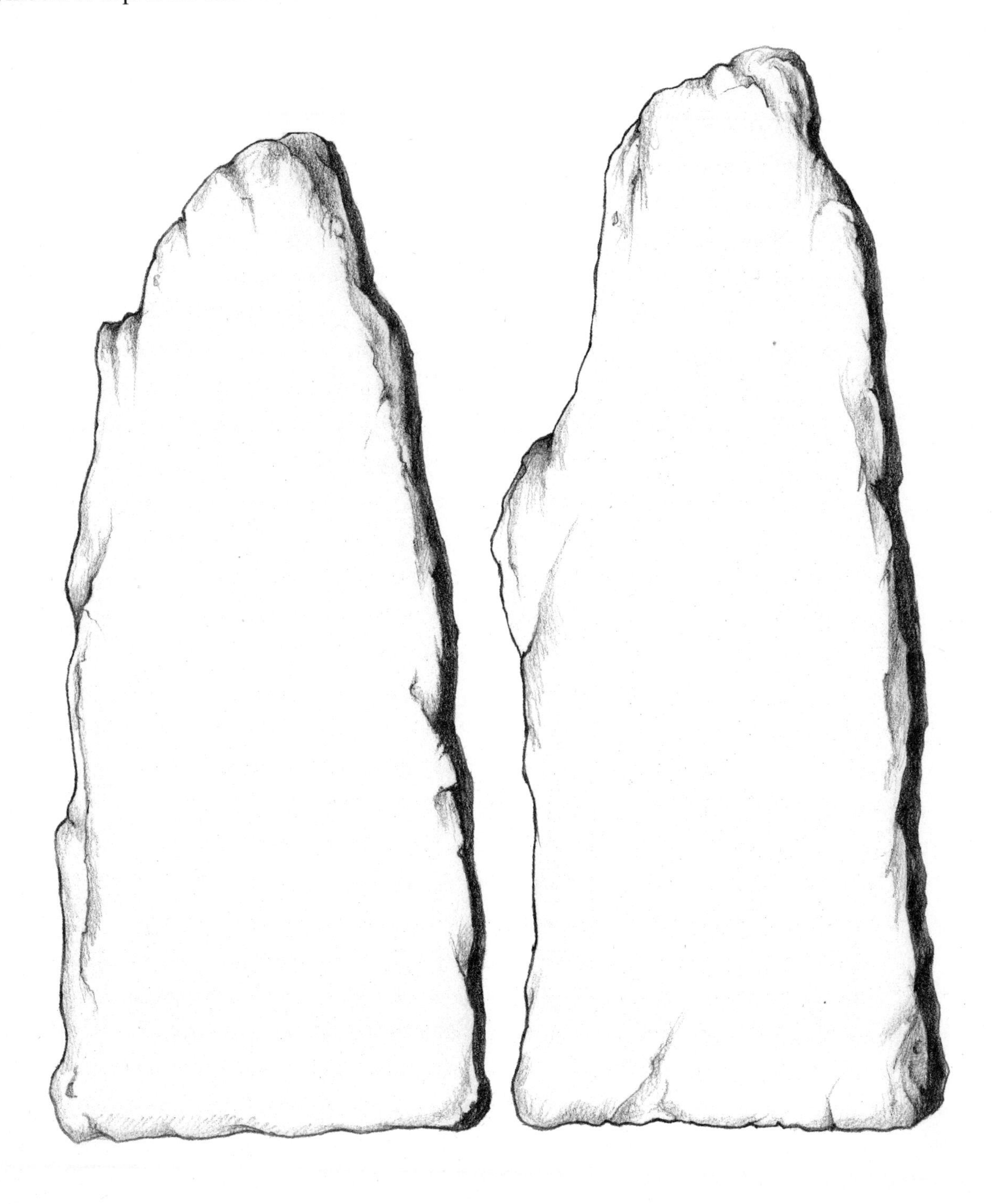

READING NOTES 6

In the steles for each empire, draw and label pictures to illustrate two achievements of that empire. Then complete the corresponding sentences.

The Akkadian Empire

6.2 The Akkadian Empire

This stele represents the Akkadian achievement of

____ .

This achievement was important because __________________

____

____ .

6.3 Life Under Akkadian Rule

This stele represents the Akkadian achievement of

____ .

This achievement was important because __________________

____

____ .

The Babylonian Empire

6.4 Hammurabi and the Babylonian Empire

This stele represents the Babylonian achievement of

____.

This achievement was important because ____________________

____

____.

6.5 Life in the Babylonian Empire

This stele represents the Babylonian achievement of

____.

This achievement was important because ____________________

____

____.

The Assyrian Empire

6.6 The Assyrian Empire

This stele represents the Assyrian achievement of

____.

This achievement was important because ____________

____

____.

6.7 Life Under the Assyrians

This stele represents the Assyrian achievement of

____.

This achievement was important because ____________

____

____.

The Neo-Babylonian Empire

6.8 The Neo-Babylonian Empire

This stele represents the Neo-Babylonian achievement of

____ .

This achievement was important because __________________

____

____ .

6.9 Life in the Neo-Babylonian Empire

This stele represents the Neo-Babylonian achievement of

____ .

This achievement was important because __________________

____

____ .

PROCESSING 6

Pretend you are a world-famous historian. You have been asked to present a report at an important historical conference on this topic: *Which Mesopotamian empire accomplished the most?*

On a separate sheet of paper, prepare a report that follows the structure outlined below. Your report should have

- an introductory paragraph in which you explain why you are an expert on this topic (you can make this information up) and clearly state your position on the question above.
- one paragraph in which you describe at least two specific examples to support your position.
- one paragraph in which you anticipate at least one argument that someone in favor of a different empire might use. In this paragraph, write an argument in response.
- a concluding paragraph in which you restate your position and briefly summarize your main supporting points.

TIMELINE CHALLENGE 1

Use the timeline below to help you complete Items A–F. When completed, each item should include the following:

- the date(s) and a short written description of the item.
- a simple symbol or drawing to represent the item.
- an appropriate geometric shape surrounding the symbol or drawing. The shapes correspond to the categories in the box above the right side of the timeline.
- a color bar or dot in the appropriate location on the timeline.
- a line connecting the bar or dot to the geometric shape.

A. 1.8 million – 200,000 B.C.E.
Homo erectus learns to make
__________ .

2 million B.C.E.	1.5 million B.C.E.	1 million B.C.E.

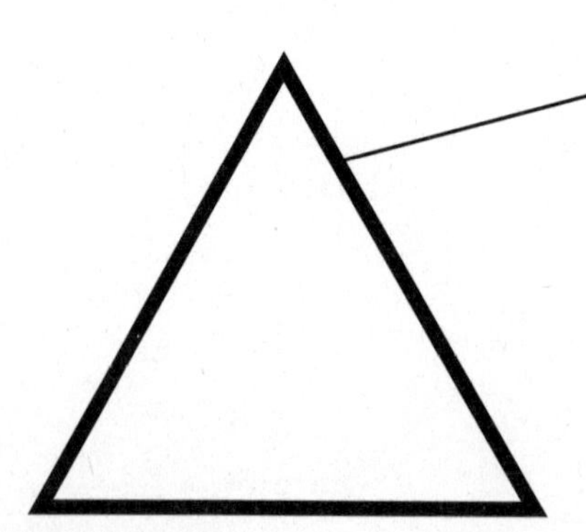

C. 6500 – 5700 B.C.E.
People in the Neolithic town of Catal Hoyuk have different jobs, such as farmer, basket weaver, and toolmaker.

TIMELINE CHALLENGE 1

△ Social Structure ◯ Government □ Religion ⬠ Arts ⯃ Technology ▱ Writing System

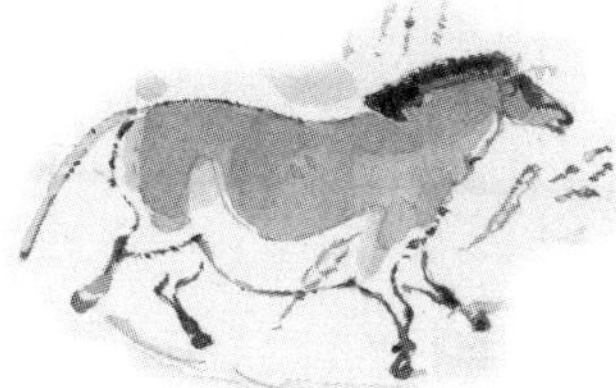

B. 35,000 – 12,000 B.C.E.
Homo sapiens sapiens artists create cave paintings.

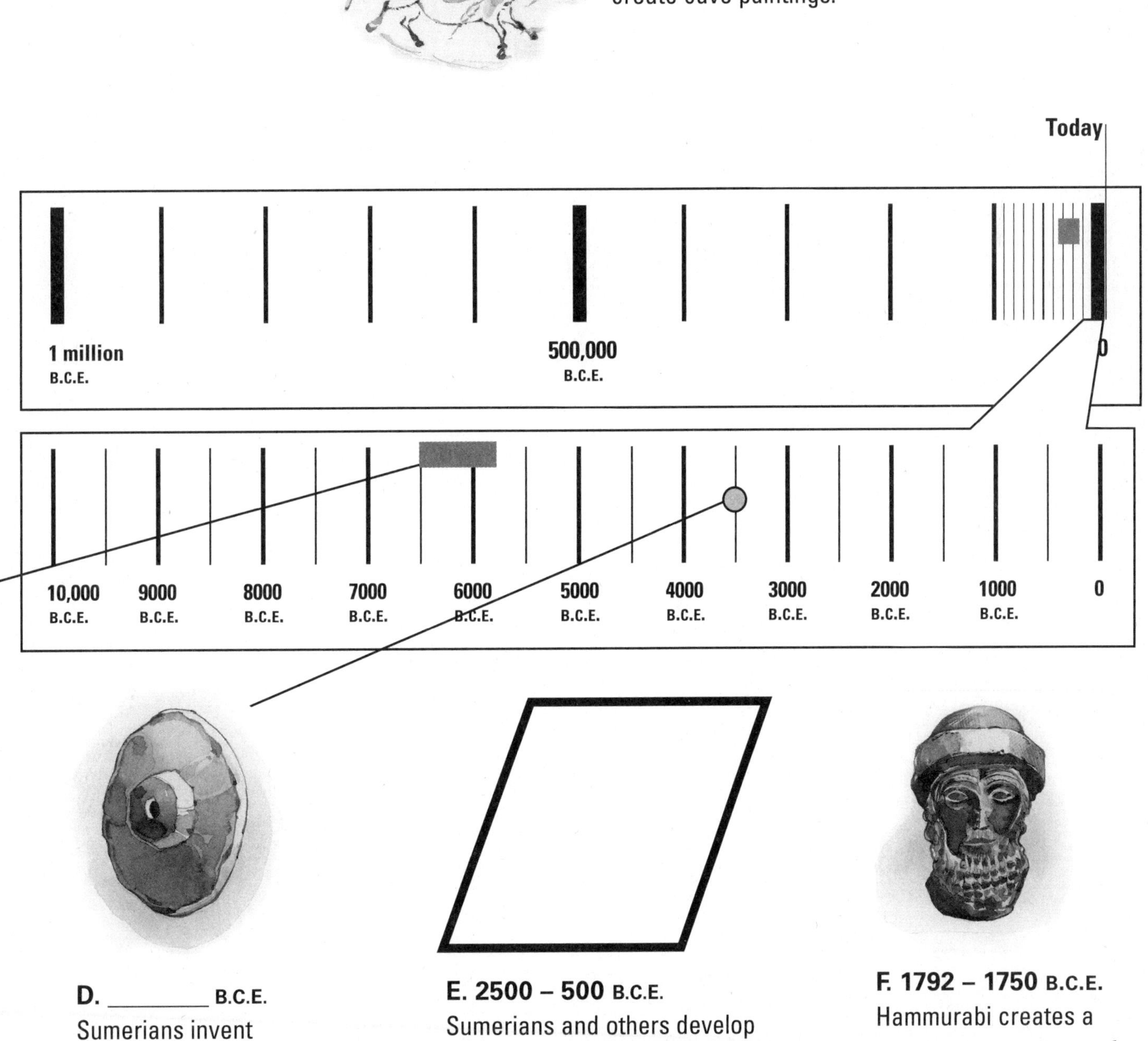

D. _________ **B.C.E.**
Sumerians invent the wheel.

E. 2500 – 500 B.C.E.
Sumerians and others develop
_____________________ .

F. 1792 – 1750 B.C.E.
Hammurabi creates a
_____________________ for
the Babylonian Empire.

UNIT 2

Ancient Egypt and the Near East

GEOGRAPHY CHALLENGE 2

To complete each Geography Challenge card, answer the questions in complete sentences. Label the map on the opposite page as directed.

Question 1 ________________________________

____

Question 2 ________________________________

____

Question 3 ________________________________

____

Question 4 ________________________________

____

Question 5 ________________________________

____

Question 6 ________________________________

____

Question 7 ________________________________

____

Question 8 ________________________________

____

GEOGRAPHY CHALLENGE 2

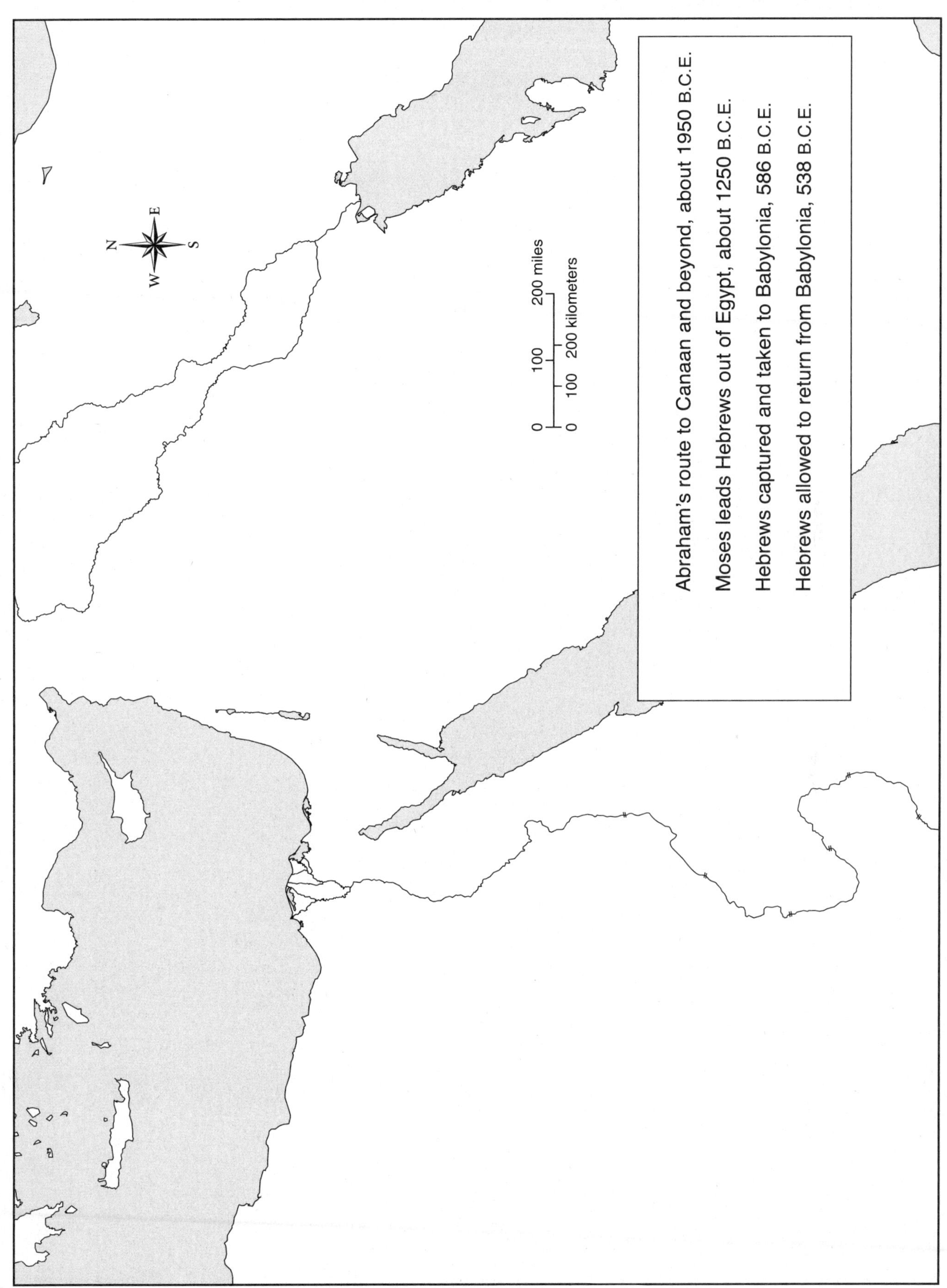

PREVIEW 7

Pretend you are living 150 years in the future. You are a member of a space-exploration expedition that has been sent to live on a far-off planet. The geography and environment of the planet are very much like that of Earth. But there are no cities, towns, or villages, or even any human beings at all.

List at least three environmental factors you would look for when selecting a place to establish your small colony. For each factor, write a short explanation of why it is important. For example, you might write, *I would look for a river to provide food and fresh water for our colony.*

Environmental Factor 1:

Environmental Factor 2:

Environmental Factor 3:

READING NOTES 7

After reading Section 7.3 and examining the map on page 68 in *History Alive! The Ancient World*, follow these steps:

1. Label the map below with these features:
   - Mediterranean Sea
   - Nile River
   - Nubian Desert
   - Red Sea
   - Libyan Desert
   - Arabian Desert
2. Write the letter H or another simple symbol in all the places on the map where human settlements were located in this region.

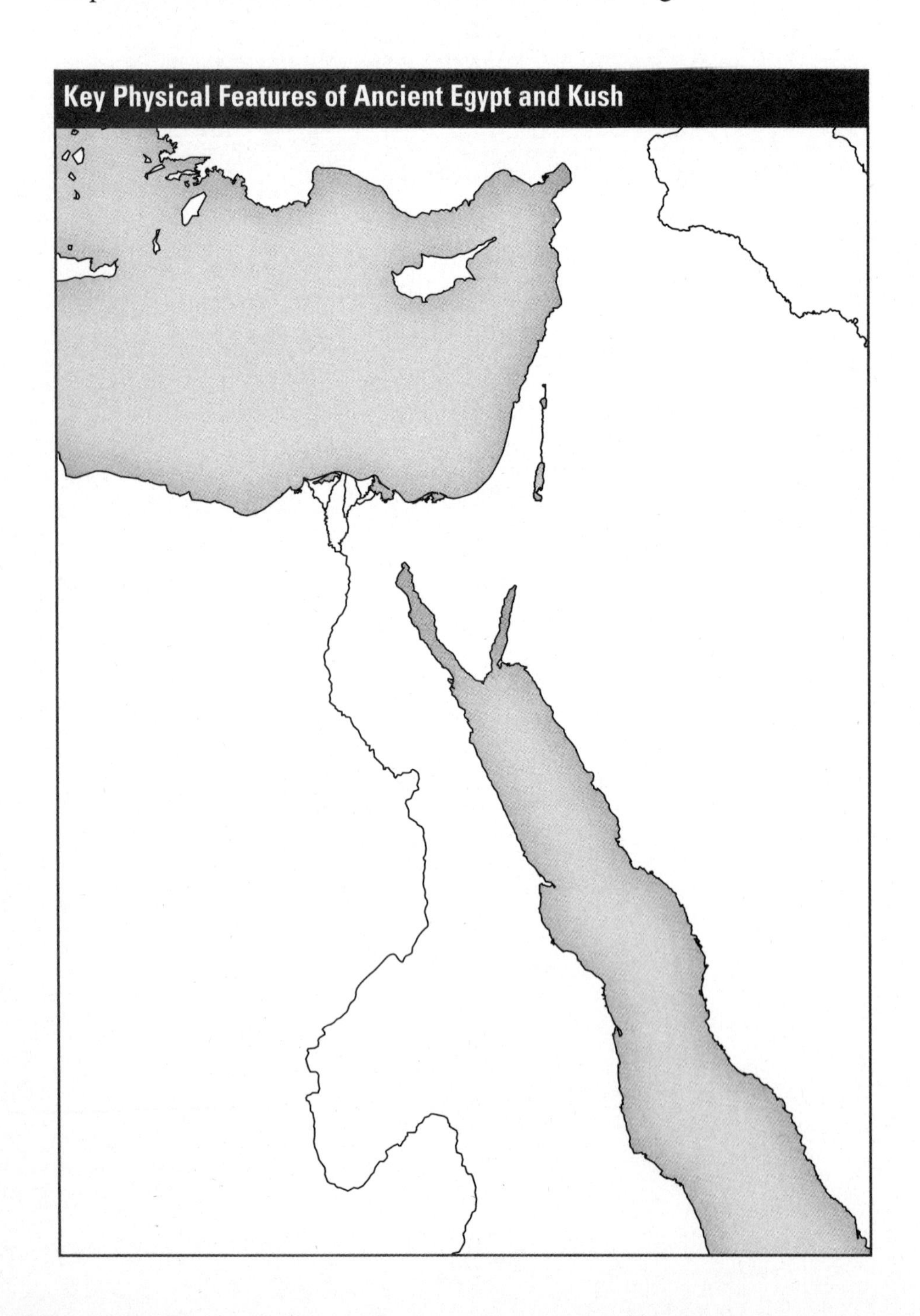

3. Write a paragraph that answers this question: *Why were human settlements located in the places you selected?* Use at least five words or phrases from the Word Bank.

Word Bank		
Mediterranean Sea	Libyan Desert	water
Red Sea	Nubian Desert	topography
Nile River	Arabian Desert	vegetation

READING NOTES 7

After reading Section 7.4 and examining the map on page 70, follow these steps:

1. Label the map below with these features:
   - Mediterranean Sea
   - Jordan River
   - Dead Sea
   - Syrian Desert
   - Sea of Galilee
   - Negev Desert
   - Lebanon Mountains
2. Write the letter H or another simple symbol in all the places on the map where human settlements were located in this region.

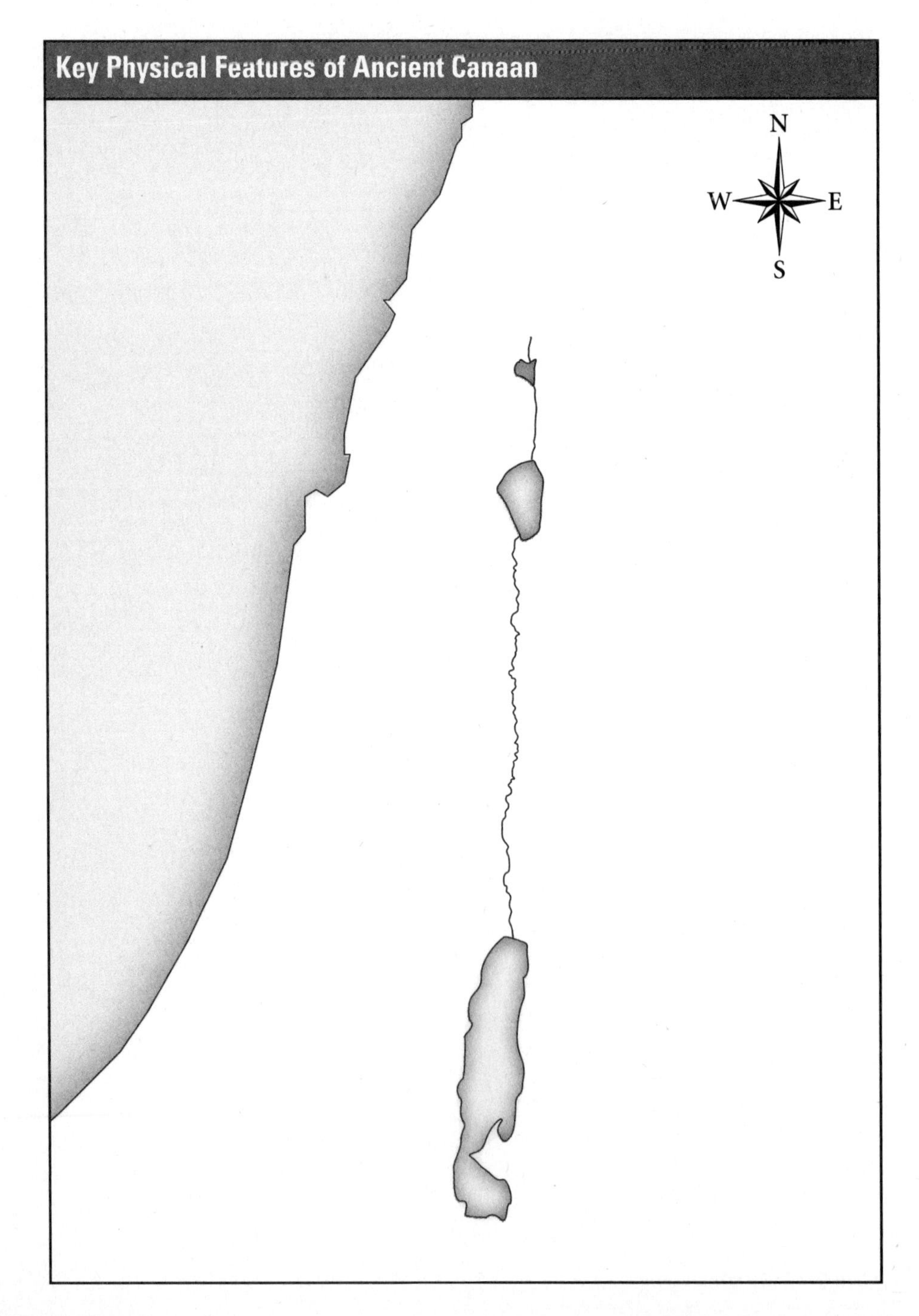

3. Write a paragraph that answers this question: *Why were human settlements located in the places you selected?* Use at least five words or phrases from the Word Bank.

Word Bank		
Mediterranean Sea	Syrian Desert	water
Sea of Galilee	Negev Desert	topography
Dead Sea	Lebanon Mountains	vegetation
Jordan River		

PROCESSING 7

In the space below, draw a simple map of the state in which you live. Your map should include the following:

- symbols and labels for at least four important physical features of your state (mountains, hills, rivers, lakes, bays, oceans, valleys, or deserts)
- stick figures or other simple symbols to show where the first human settlements were most likely located

Now write a short paragraph to answer this question: *Why would human settlements likely be located in the places you selected?* Your answer should include the names of at least two of the important physical features of your state *and* at least two of these terms: *water, topography, vegetation.*

PREVIEW 8

Carefully analyze the postcard. As your teacher reveals each question, discuss it with your partners and write your answers below.

1.

2.

3.

4.

5.

READING NOTES 8

For each site you visit on your felucca tour, send a postcard to a friend or relative. Follow these steps to create each postcard:

1. Begin with a proper greeting (such as *Dear Maria,*).
2. Fill in the blank with the name of the monument.
3. Write at least one interesting thing you learned about the monument.
4. Fill in the blank with name of pharaoh.
5. Write at least one interesting thing you learned about the pharaoh.
6. Draw an appropriate symbol or visual for the stamp.
7. Write a proper closing (such as *See you soon!*).

Tour Site 1

Dear ____________,

The monument I just visited is ________________________

____

____

It was built by the pharaoh ________________________

____

____

Tour Site 2

Dear ____________,

The monument I just visited is ____________________

____

____

It was built by the pharaoh ____________________

____

____

Tour Site 3

Dear ____________,

The monument I just visited is ____________________

____

____

It was built by the pharaoh ____________________

____

____

Tour Site 4

Dear ____________ ,

The monument I just visited is ______________________

____

____

It was built by the pharaoh ______________________

____

____

Copy the name of each individual or group listed below onto the level of the pyramid where you think it belongs. For each name, write a short sentence to explain why you placed it at that level on the pyramid.

Students	Principal	Teachers	Student Council	Office Staff

My School's Social Pyramid

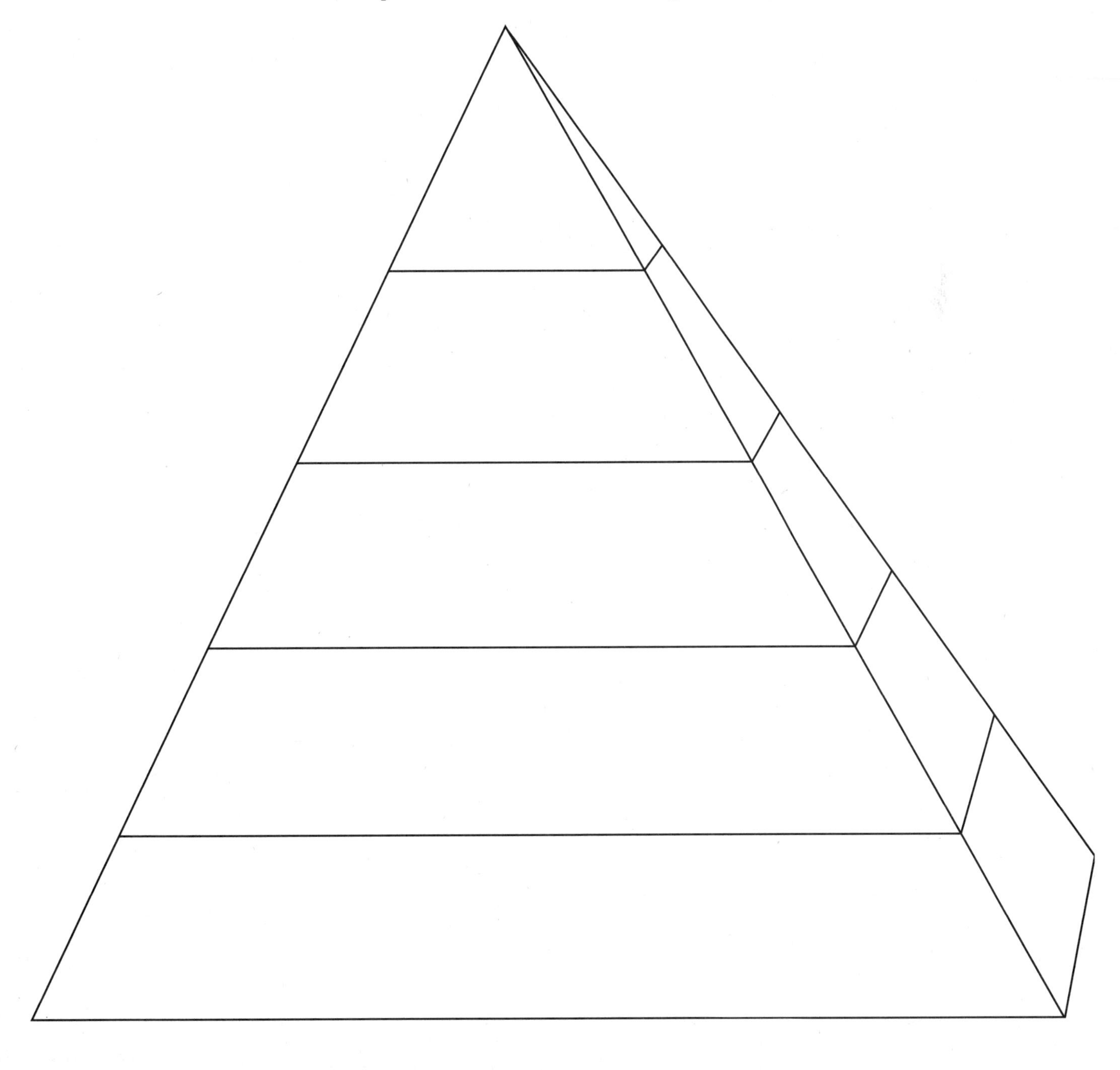

READING NOTES 9

Read Sections 9.3–9.7 in *History Alive! The Ancient World*. For each section, write four things you learned about daily life for the members of that social class.

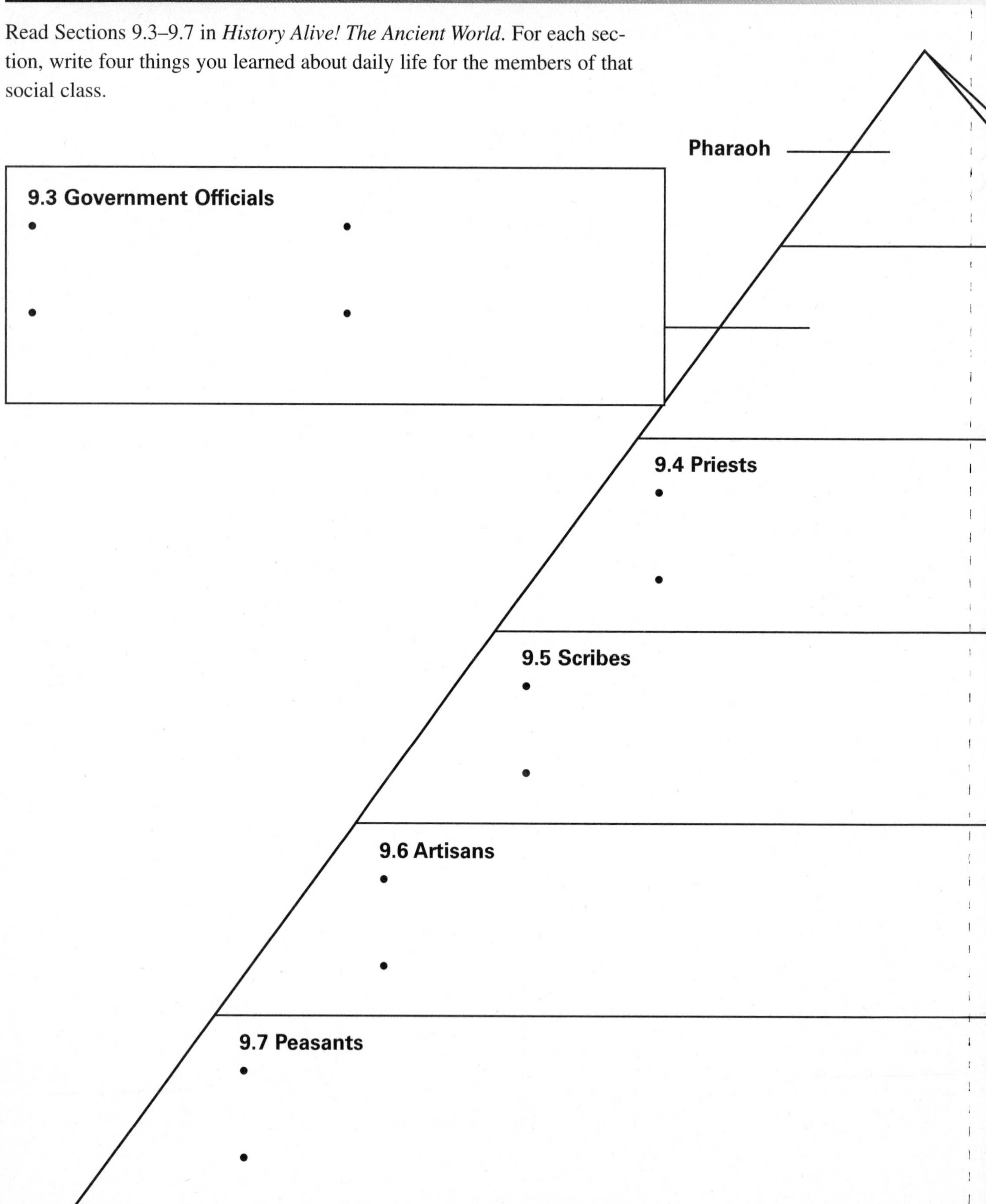

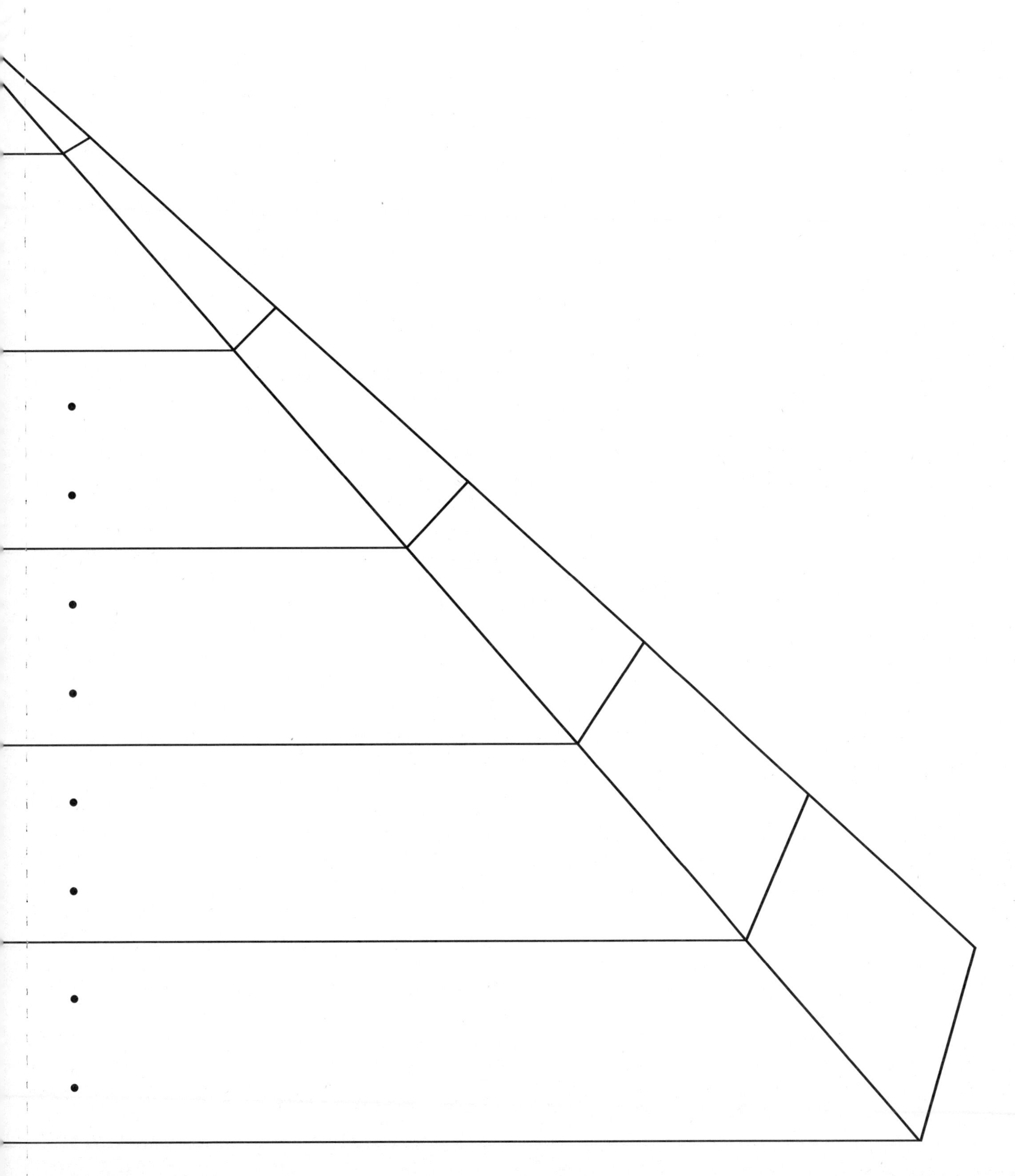

PROCESSING 9

Complete the social pyramid below by identifying a person or group in our society that is like each of the ancient Egyptian social classes listed. Explain how the modern group is similar to the ancient Egyptian social class. Finally, draw or glue an image of the modern person or group into the appropriate level of the pyramid. An example is done for you.

Egyptian government officials were like ____________________________

because…

Egyptian priests were like ____________________________

because…

Egyptian scribes were like ____________________________

because…

Egyptian artisans were like ____________________________

because…

Egyptian peasant farmers were like ____________________________

because…

PROCESSING 9

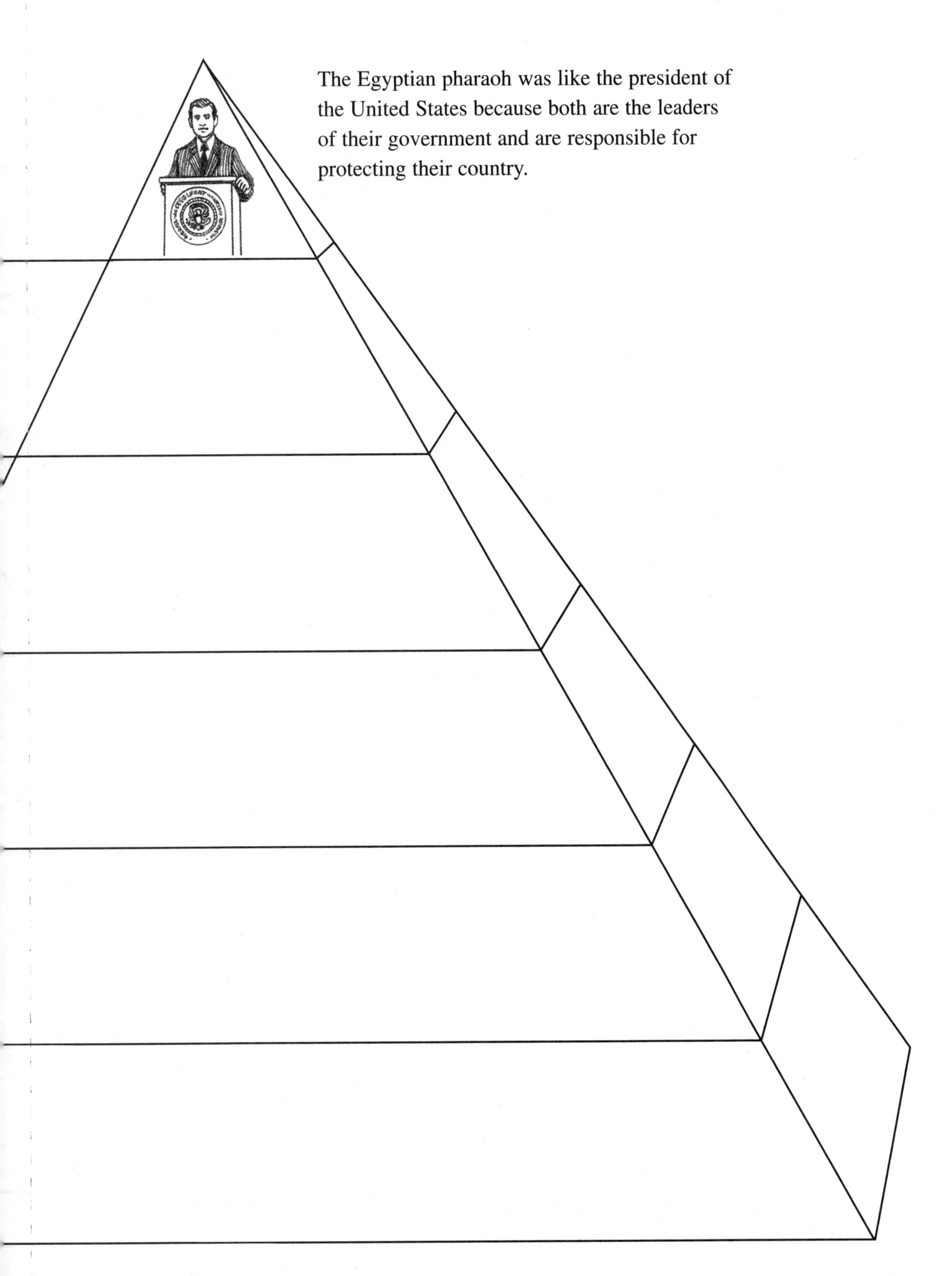

The Egyptian pharaoh was like the president of the United States because both are the leaders of their government and are responsible for protecting their country.

PREVIEW 10

A sensory figure is a simple drawing of a character with short descriptions of what that character sees, hears, touches, and feels. Follow these directions to create a sensory figure in the space below:

- Draw and label a simple outline of an important current leader of your country, such as the president.
- Finish the statement in each box to describe four important things this person has seen, heard, touched, and felt (emotions) during his or her time as a leader. Draw a line from each statement to an appropriate part of the figure.

With my eyes, I see...

With my ears, I hear...

With my hands, I touch...

With my heart, I feel...

READING NOTES 10

10.2 The Egyptianization of Kush

For the sensory figure below, finish the statements to describe four important things a Kush leader would have seen, heard, touched, and felt (emotions) during this period of Kush history. In your statements, include and underline all the words from the Word Bank. Use each word only once. One example is done for you.

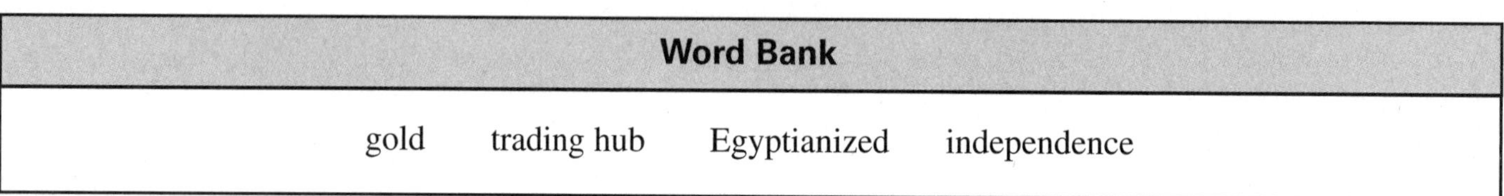

Word Bank			
gold	trading hub	Egyptianized	independence

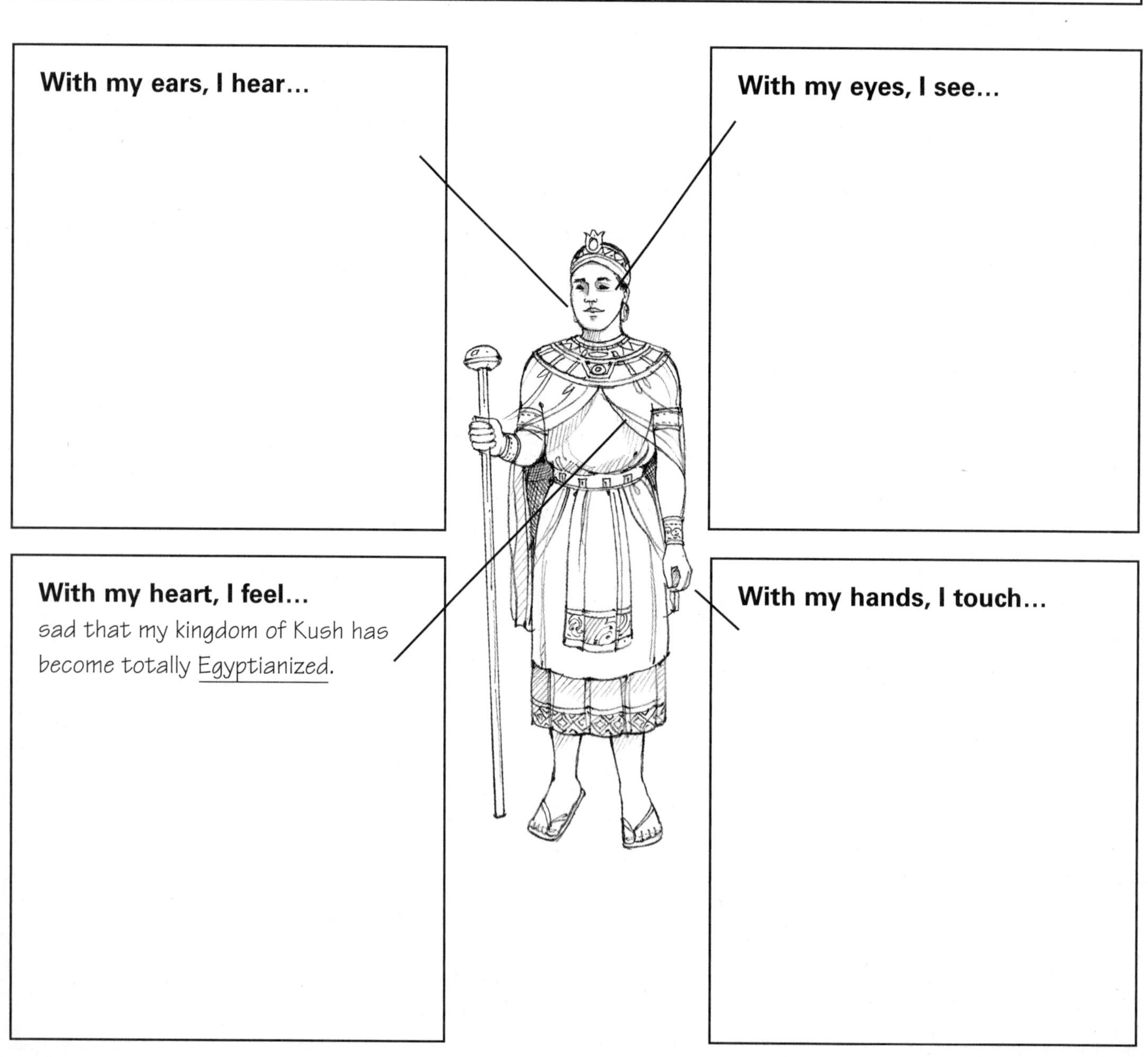

READING NOTES 10

10.3 Kush Conquers Egypt

For the sensory figure below, finish the statements to describe four important things a Kush leader would have seen, heard, touched, and felt during this period of Kush history. Be sure to include and underline all the words from the Word Bank. Use each word only once.

Word Bank			
invaders	Kushite pharaohs	Jebel Barkal	Assyrians

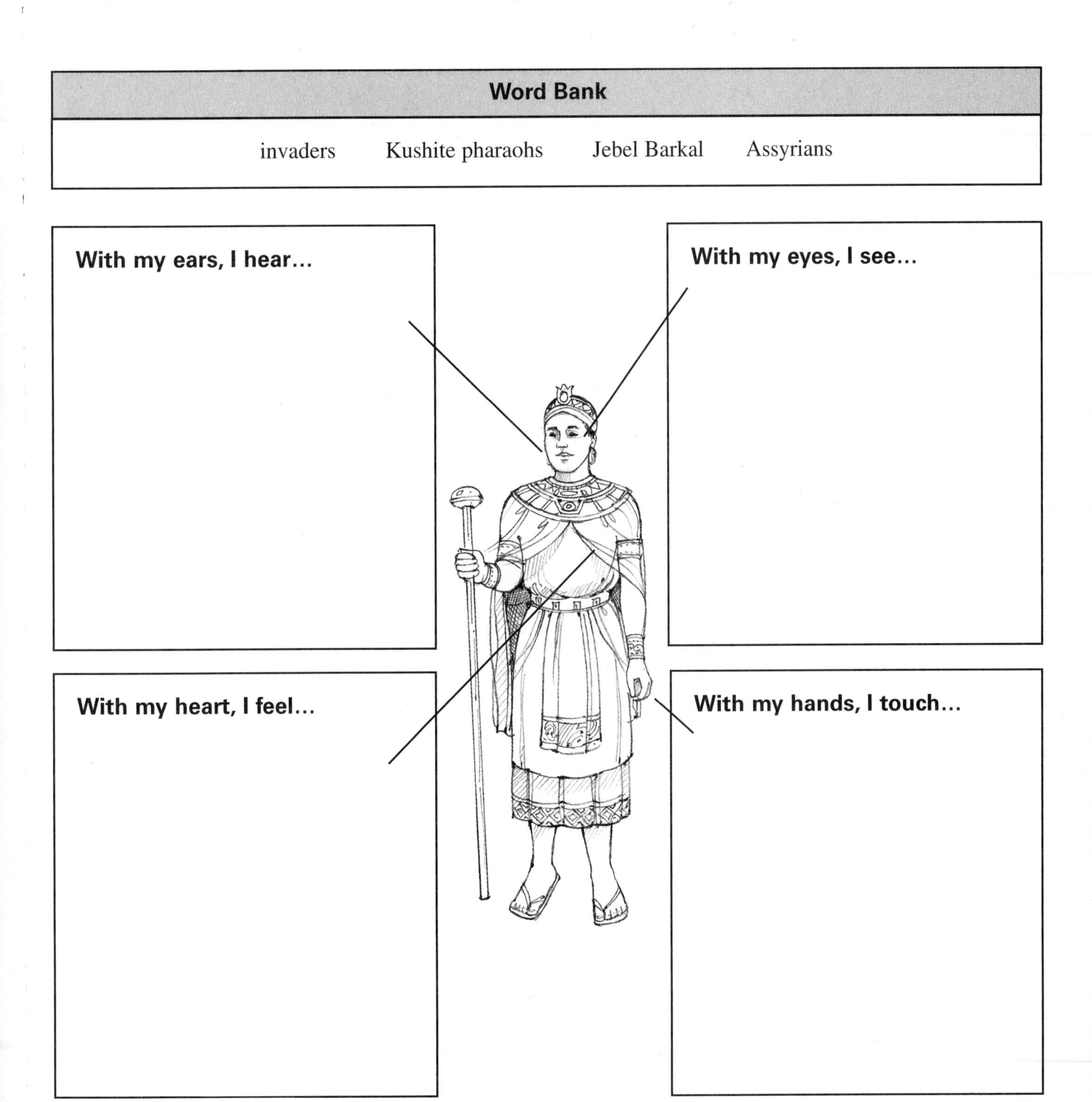

10.4 The Kush Capital of Meroë

For the sensory figure below, finish the statements to describe four important things a Kush leader would have seen, heard, touched, and felt during this period of Kush history. Be sure to include and underline all the words and phrases from the Word Bank. Use each word only once.

Word Bank
Meroë   trade   iron   weapons and tools

10.5 Kush Returns to Its African Roots

For the sensory figure below, finish the statements to describe four important things a Kush leader would have seen, heard, touched, and felt during this period of Kush history. Be sure to include and underline all the words from the Word Bank. Use each word only once.

Word Bank
African Meroitic kandake Romans

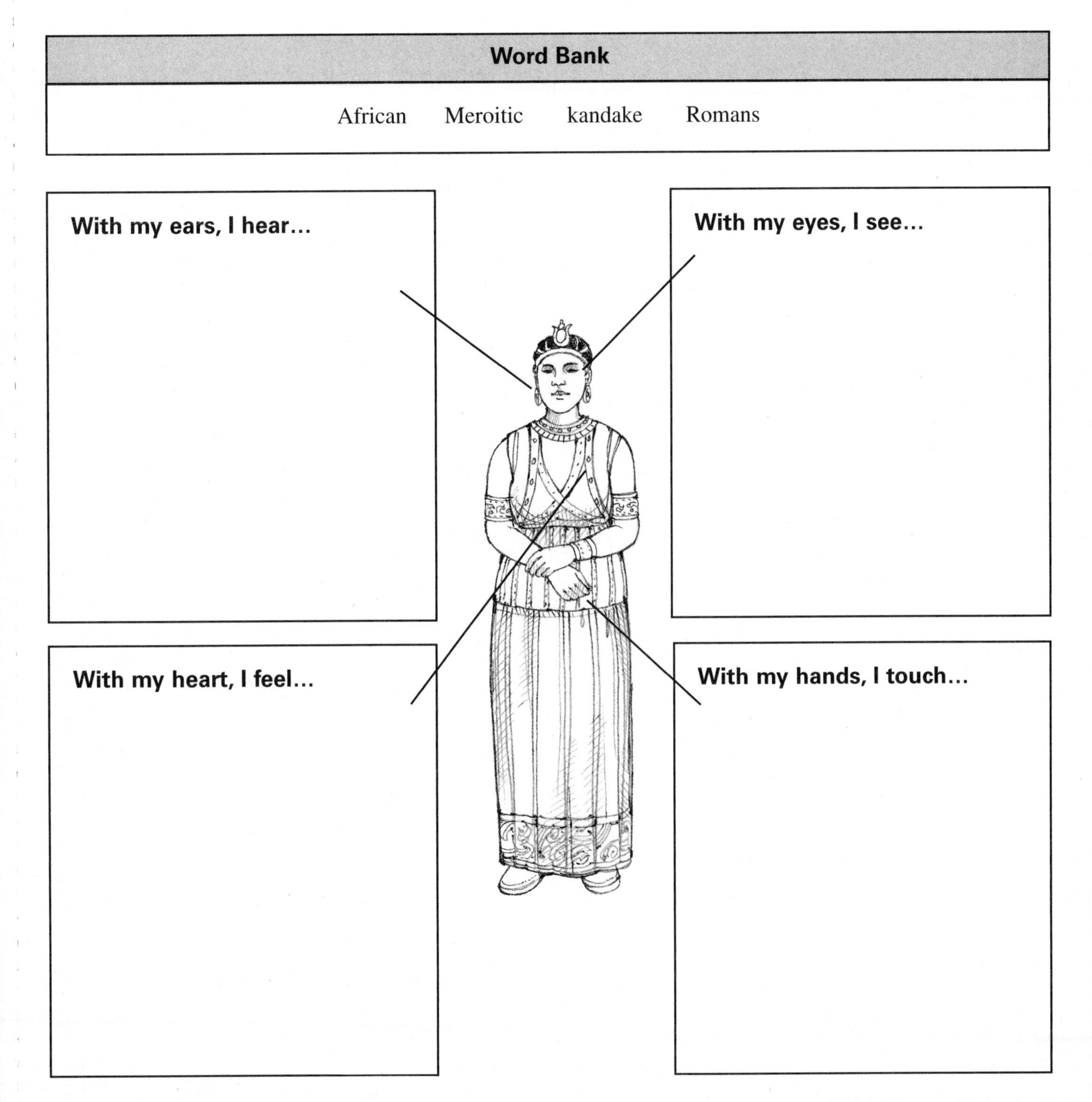

PROCESSING 10

Pretend that the leader you drew in Preview 10 could meet with one of the Kush leaders you learned about in this chapter. Complete a "talking" Venn diagram of these two leaders by following these steps:

- Label each leader. Then add details, such as clothing and hair, to the outlines of the leader you drew in the Preview.
- In the area between the two leaders where the speech bubbles overlap, write at least two things the leaders would say their country and kingdom have in common.
- In the areas that do not overlap, write at least two things the leaders would say are different about their country and kingdom. Write at least two statements for *each* leader.

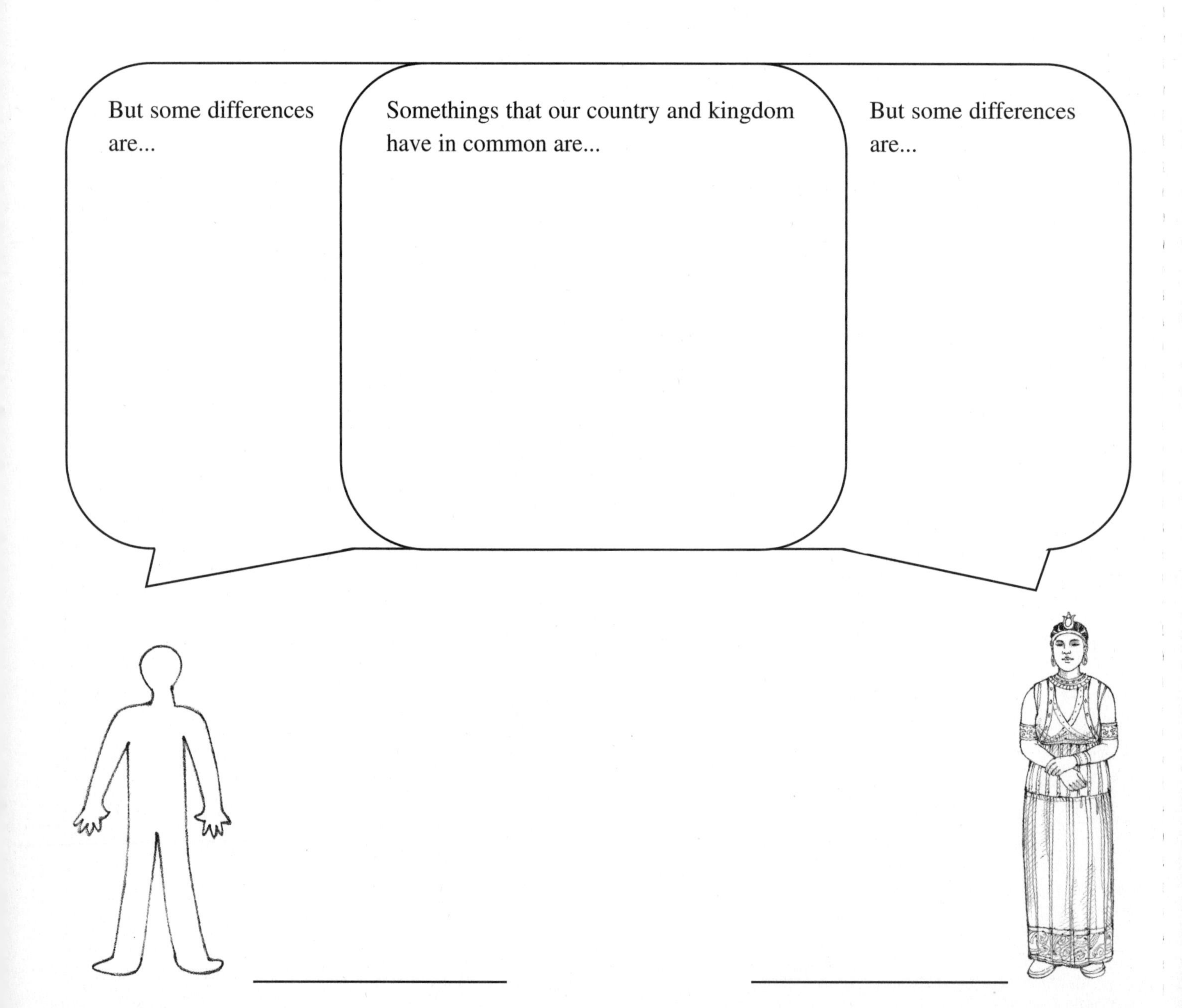

PREVIEW 11

Think of three figures who have been important in the development of the United States. List them below. Then write a sentence that explains that person's role in the development of this country, and draw a symbol to represent it. An example is given for you.

Alice Paul
She led the fight for women to have the right to vote, which was finally achieved in 1920.

Figure 1: ______________________________

Figure 2: ______________________________

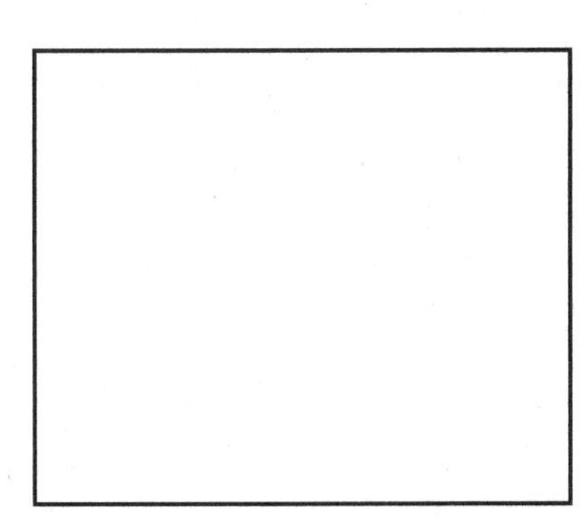

Figure 3: ______________________________

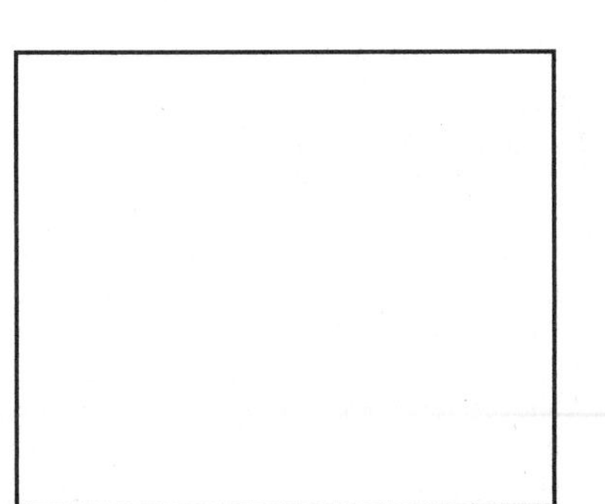

READING NOTES 11

Read Section 11.4 of *History Alive! The Ancient World* and complete the scroll below.

11.4 The Life of Abraham: Father of the Hebrews

1. Describe an important action taken by Abraham.

2. List at least two contributions Abraham made to the development of Judaism.
   •
   •

3. Write a quotation from the Torah that shows one of these contributions.

4. Sketch a key artifact related to Abraham.

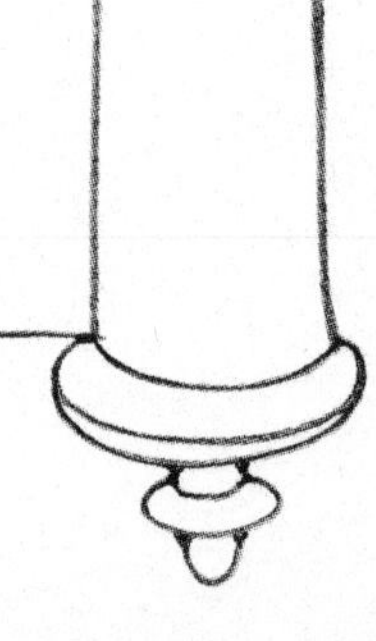

Read Section 11.5 of *History Alive! The Ancient World* and complete the scroll below.

11.5 The Life of Moses: Leader and Prophet

Moses משׁה

1. Describe an important action taken by Moses.

2. List at least two contributions Moses made to the development of Judaism.
   -
   -

3. Write a quotation from the Torah that shows one of these contributions.

4. Sketch a key artifact related to Moses.

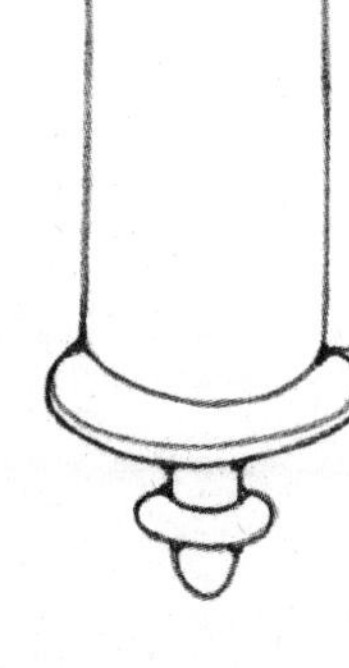

READING NOTES 11

Read Section 11.6 of *History Alive! The Ancient World* and complete the scroll below.

11.6 The Lives of David and Solomon: Kings of Israel

David דוד Solomon שׁלמה

1. Describe an important action taken by David or Solomon.

2. List at least two contributions David and Solomon made to the development of Judaism.
   -
   -

3. Write a quotation from the Hebrew Bible that shows one of these contributions.

4. Sketch a key artifact related to David or Solomon.

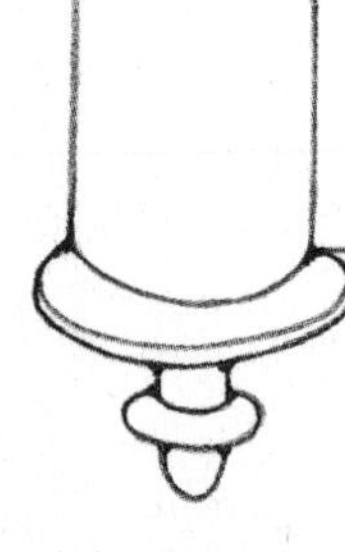

READING NOTES 12

Read Section 12.2 in *History Alive! The Ancient World*. Complete the notes below by identifying four similarities between the classroom activity and the history of Judaism. One example is done for you.

12.2 The Central Beliefs and Teachings of Judaism	
The Classroom Activity	The History of Judaism
• The first classroom truth we learned about was that our class has only one true teacher.	• The first central belief of Judaism, monotheism, is that there is only one God.
•	•
•	•
•	•

READING NOTES 12

Read Section 12.3. Complete the notes below by identifying two or more similarities between the classroom activity and the history of Judaism.

12.3 Foreign Domination and the Jewish Diaspora	
The Classroom Activity	The History of Judaism
•	•
•	•
•	•
•	•

READING NOTES 12

Read Section 12.4. Complete the notes below by identifying three or more similarities between the classroom activity and the history of Judaism.

12.4 Preserving and Passing On the Teachings of Judaism	
The Classroom Activity	The History of Judaism
• • • •	• • • •

PROCESSING 12

Find a newspaper or magazine article about a current topic that reflects one of the four central beliefs or teachings of Judaism. Paste the headline or article into the space below. Below the article, write a paragraph that tells which beliefs or teachings the article reflects and how.

TIMELINE CHALLENGE 2

Use the timeline below to help you complete Items A–F. When completed, each item should include the following:

- the date(s) and a short written description of the item.
- a simple symbol or drawing to represent the item.
- an appropriate geometric shape surrounding the symbol or drawing. The shapes correspond to the categories listed above the right side of the timeline.
- a color bar or dot in the appropriate location on the timeline.
- a line connecting the bar or dot to the geometric shape.

B. 1544 – ________ B.C.E.
Society is structured like a pyramid during Egypt's New Kingdom.

A. ________ B.C.E.
Egyptian hieroglyphics are developed.

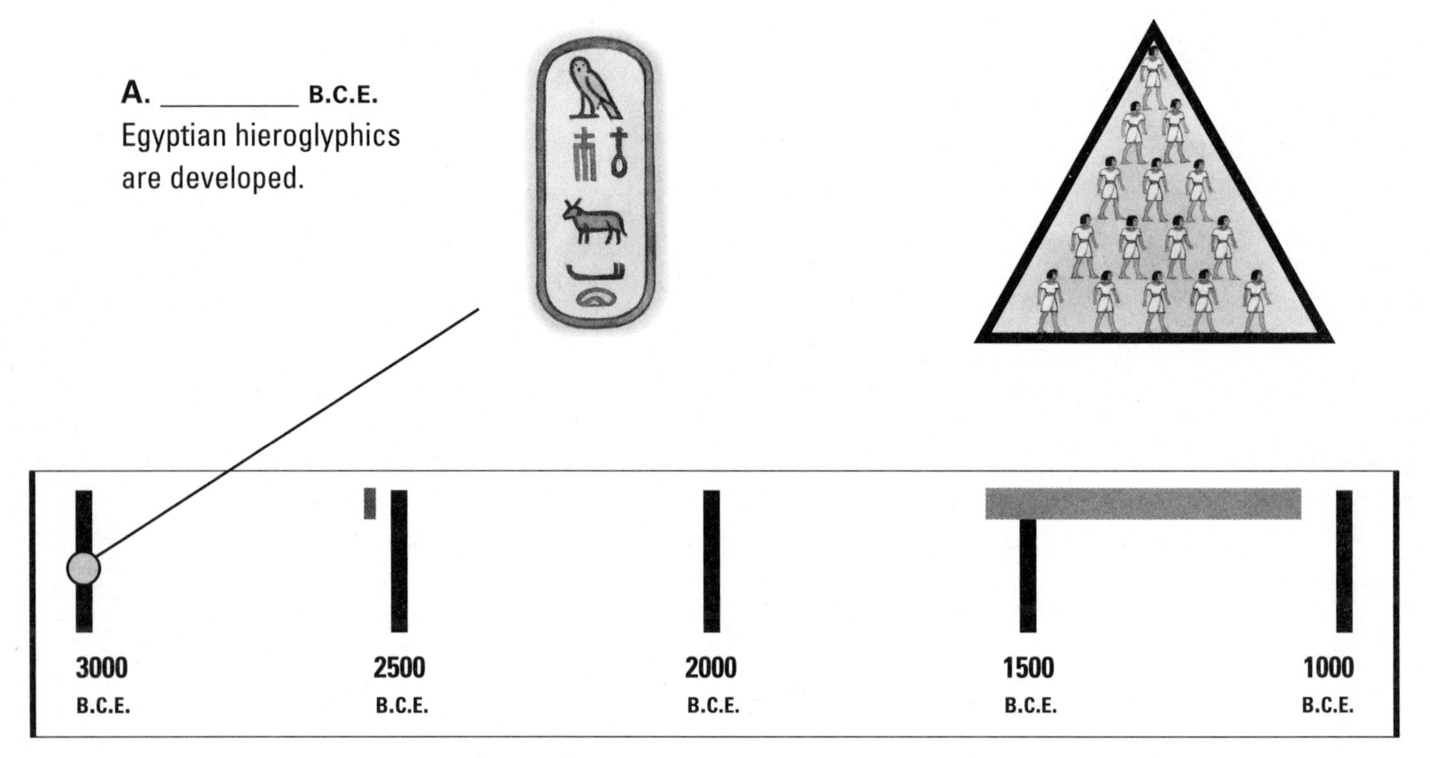

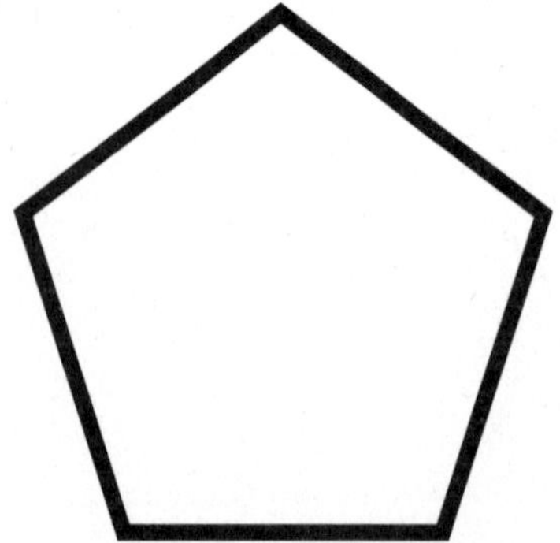

D. 2551 – 2528 B.C.E.
The Great Pyramid is built in Egypt.

△ Social Structure ○ Government □ Religion ⬠ Arts ⬡ Technology ▱ Writing System

C. 24 B.C.E.
Kandake Amanirenas defends
Kush against Roman armies.

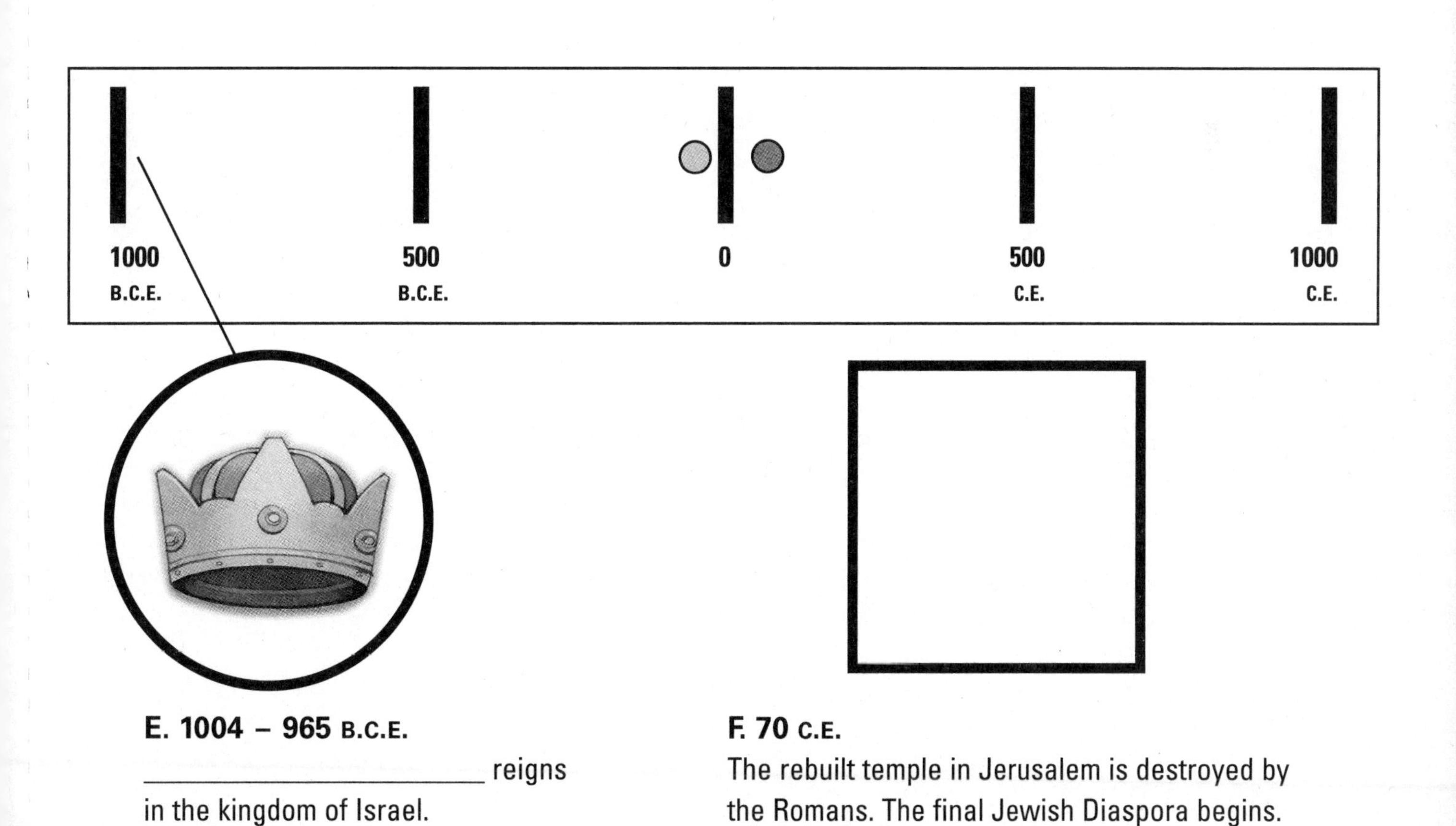

E. 1004 – 965 B.C.E.
________________________ reigns
in the kingdom of Israel.

F. 70 C.E.
The rebuilt temple in Jerusalem is destroyed by
the Romans. The final Jewish Diaspora begins.

UNIT 3

Ancient India

GEOGRAPHY CHALLENGE 3

To complete each Geography Challenge card, answer the questions in complete sentences. Label the map on the opposite page as directed.

Question 1 ____________________

____

Question 2 ____________________

____

Question 3 ____________________

____

Question 4 ____________________

____

Question 5 ____________________

____

Question 6 ____________________

____

Question 7 ____________________

____

Question 8 ____________________

____

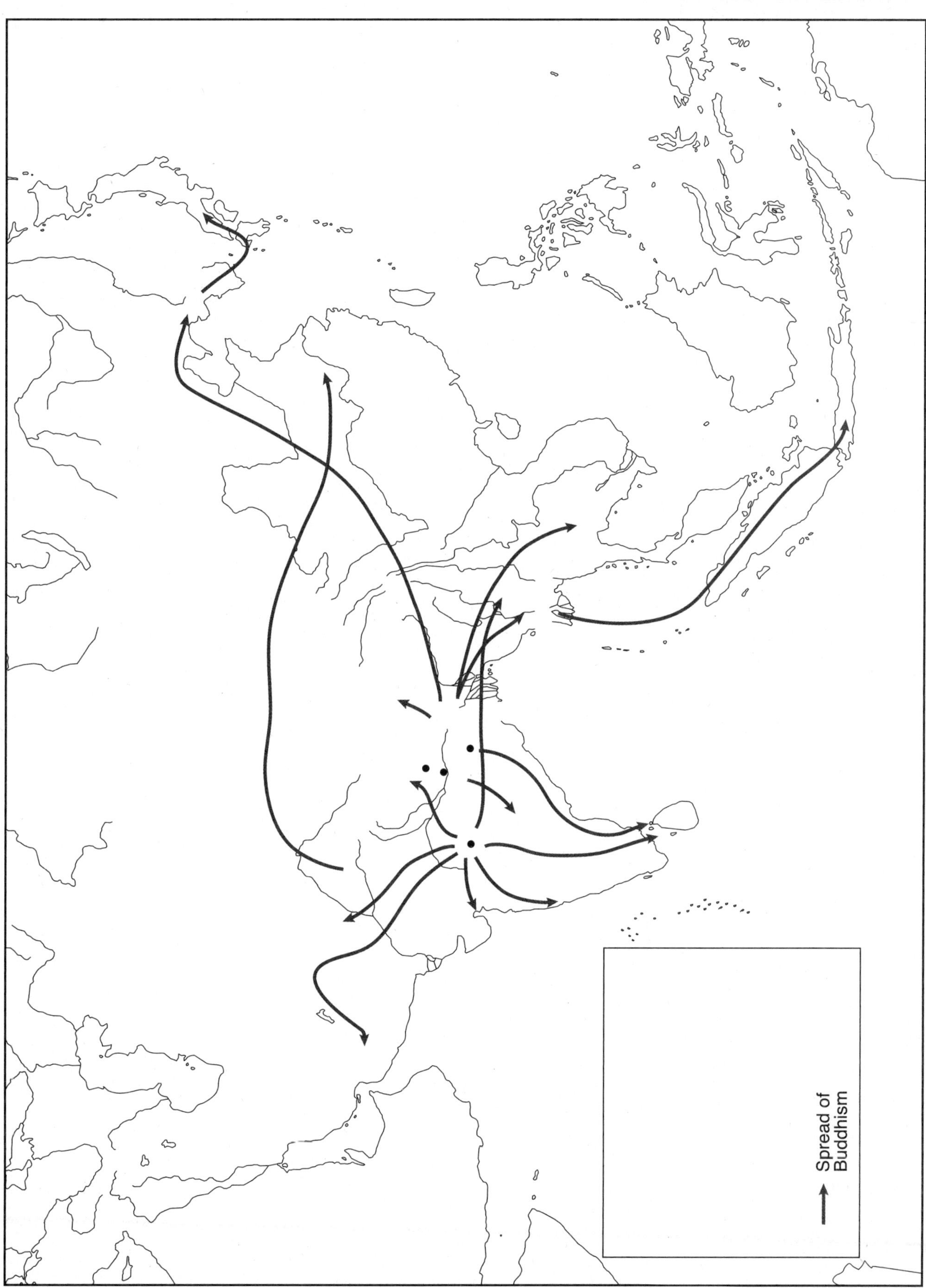
Spread of Buddhism

PREVIEW 13

You are a member of a group of people living in ancient times. Your group needs to move, and you have been chosen to find a new location where the group can resettle. You travel around until you find the perfect spot. No one lives there, and it has everything your group needs. What a place! Now you have to convince the others that this is the right place.

In the space below, draw and label a picture of the place you have found. Show what you would find in an ideal place to settle.

READING NOTES 13

For each physical feature, follow these steps:

- Read about the feature in your book. Take turns reading aloud.
- In the table below, enter the name of the feature.
- Write a brief description of the feature.
- In the appropriate place on the map, color and label the feature.
- With your partner, discuss the rating of the feature on a scale of 1 to 5, with 1 meaning "unsuitable for settlement" and 5 meaning "very suitable for settlement." Enter your rating in the table.

Physical Feature	Description	Rating

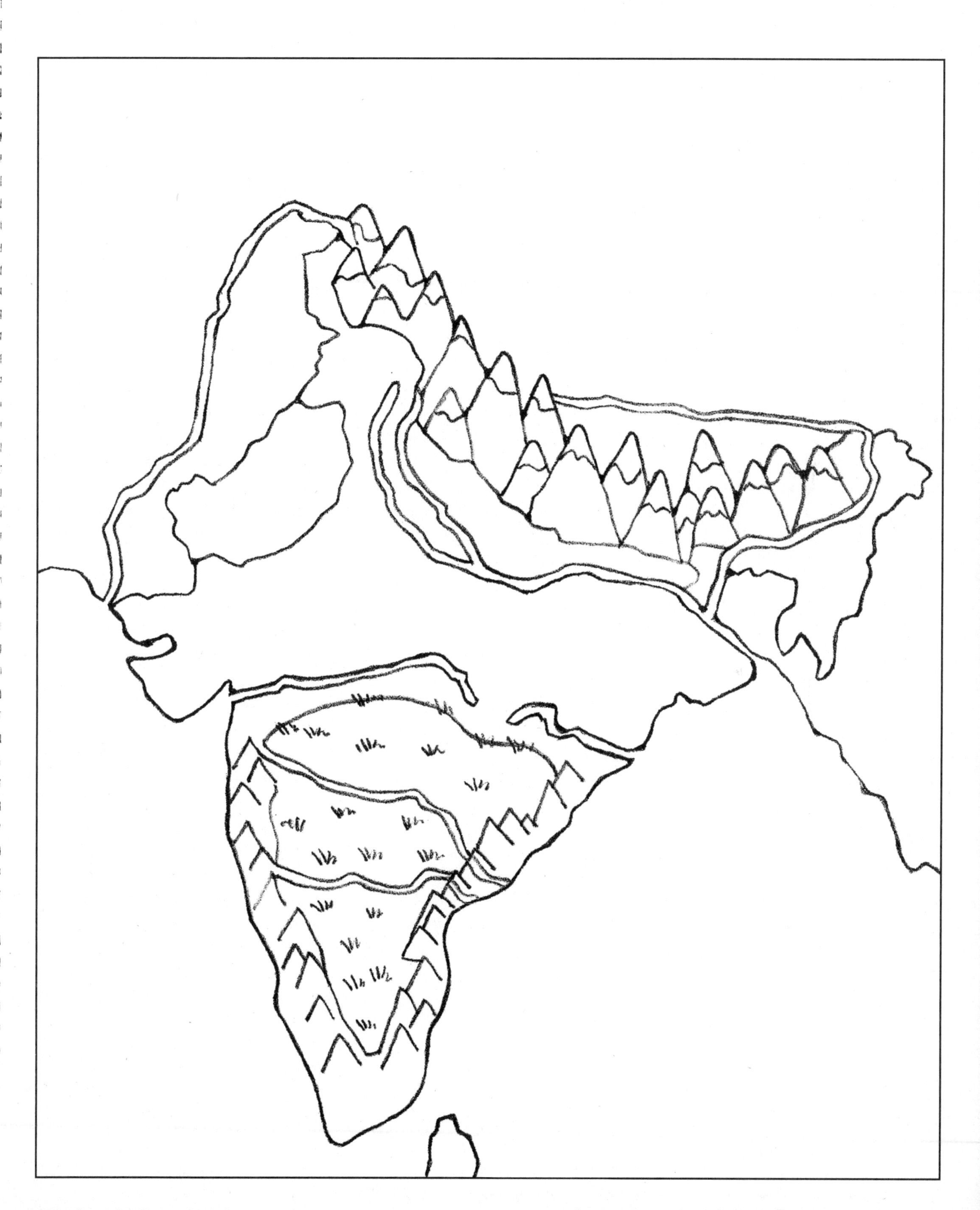

PROCESSING 13

Design a real estate advertisement to convince people to settle near one of the eight physical features you studied in this activity. Include these things in your advertisement:

- a catchy slogan
- three great reasons to settle in this place
- an illustration of the location

PREVIEW 14

Based on the arguments presented by your four classmates, which of the four options below do you think is the true description of the object? Circle your choice, and explain your answer.

I think this object is

- a petrified bagel (one so old that it has become as hard as a rock)
- a heavy bracelet
- a form of money
- an ancient toilet seat

I think this because...

READING NOTES 14

Station A

1. Complete the drawing.

2. Record your ideas about what these objects may have been used for.

3. Read Section 14.3. Record the archeologists' ideas about these objects.

Station B

2. Record your ideas about what this structure may have been used for.

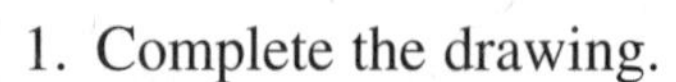

1. Complete the drawing.

3. Read Section 14.4. Record the archeologists' ideas about this structure.

Station C

1. Complete the drawings.

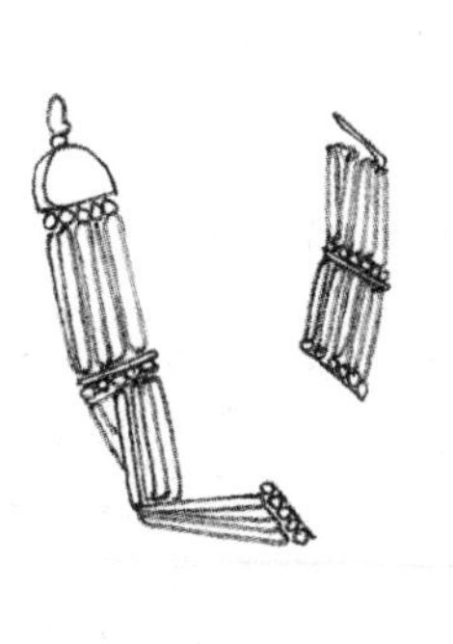

2. Record your ideas about what these objects may have been used for.

3. Read Section 14.5. Record the archeologists' ideas about these objects.

Station D

1. Complete the drawings.

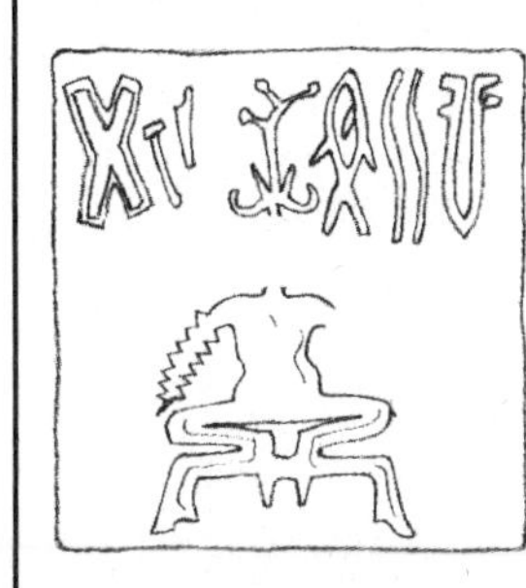

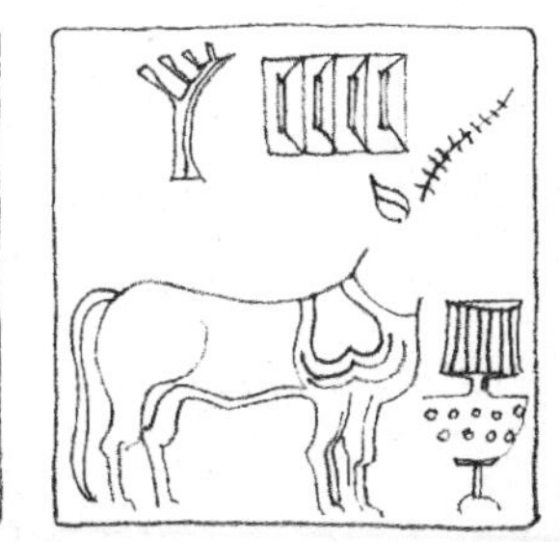

2. Record your ideas about what these objects may have been used for.

3. Read Section 14.6. Record the archeologists' ideas about these objects.

READING NOTES 14

Station E

1. Complete the drawing.

2. Record your ideas about what this structure may have been used for.

3. Read Section 14.7. Record the archeologists' ideas about this structure.

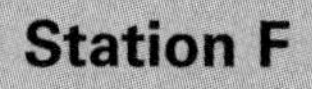

Station F

2. Record your ideas about what these structures may have been used for.

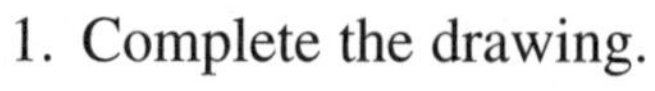

1. Complete the drawing.

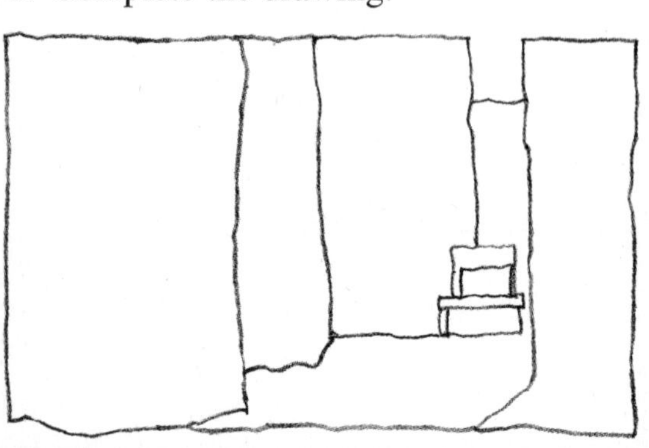

3. Read Section 14.8. Record the archeologists' ideas about these structures.

Station G

1. Complete the drawing.

2. Record your ideas about what these objects may have been used for.

3. Read Section 14.9. Record the archeologists' ideas about these objects.

Station H

1. Complete the drawing.

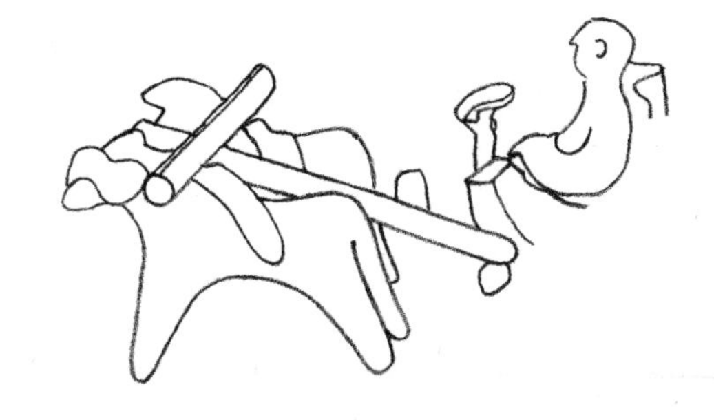

2. Record your ideas about what this object may have been used for.

3. Read Section 14.10. Record the archeologists' ideas about this object.

PROCESSING 14

Create a cover for an issue of *Dig It!* magazine that highlights the archeological discoveries made at Mohenjodaro. Your cover must include

- an imaginative subtitle.
- attractive visuals of three artifacts.
- brief captions that explain what each artifact reveals about daily life in Mohenjodaro.

PREVIEW 15

Think about how religion affects life in the United States. On the map below, draw a picture or symbol that represents one way religion affects life in the United States.

READING NOTES 15

For each of Sections 15.4–15.8, follow these steps:

Step 1. Read the section and carefully examine the transparency.

Step 2. Match the belief you just read about to one of the symbols in the mandala.

Step 3. Raise your hand when you have made a match, and silently check your answer with your teacher.

Step 4. In the box for that section, draw the mandala symbol in the circle.

Step 5. Follow the directions in the box to record notes about what you've read.

15.4 Hindu Beliefs About Brahman

Record two key points about this belief.

Describe two clues in the transparency or mandala that helped you make a match.

One effect of this belief on life in India is

15.5 Hindu Beliefs About Deities

Record two key points about this belief.

Describe two clues in the transparency or mandala that helped you make a match.

One effect of this belief on life in India is

15.6 Hindu Beliefs About Dharma

Record two key points about this belief.

Describe two clues in the transparency or mandala that helped you make a match.

One effect of this belief on life in India is

15.7 Hindu Beliefs About Karma

Record two key points about this belief.

Describe two clues in the transparency or mandala that helped you make a match.

One effect of this belief on life in India is

15.8 Hindu Beliefs About Samsara

Record two key points about this belief.

Describe two clues in the transparency or mandala that helped you make a match.

One effect of this belief on life in India is

PROCESSING 15

Create an acrostic for the word *Hinduism*. Your acrostic should include

- words, phrases, or sentences for each letter in the word *Hinduism*.
- the terms *Brahman, multiple gods, dharma, karma,* and *samsara*.
- three ways Hinduism has affected life in India.

S

M

PREVIEW 16

What do you think is the secret to happiness?

Answer the question by filling in the thought bubble below with words and simple illustrations.

READING NOTES 16

For each of Sections 16.2–16.6, follow these steps:

Step 1. Around the drawing, write sentences about the important actions and individuals in the drawing. Use the words below the drawing in your sentences, and underline them.

Step 2. On page 111, write a caption that summarizes this step along Siddhartha's path to enlightenment.

16.2 Prince Siddhartha's Birth

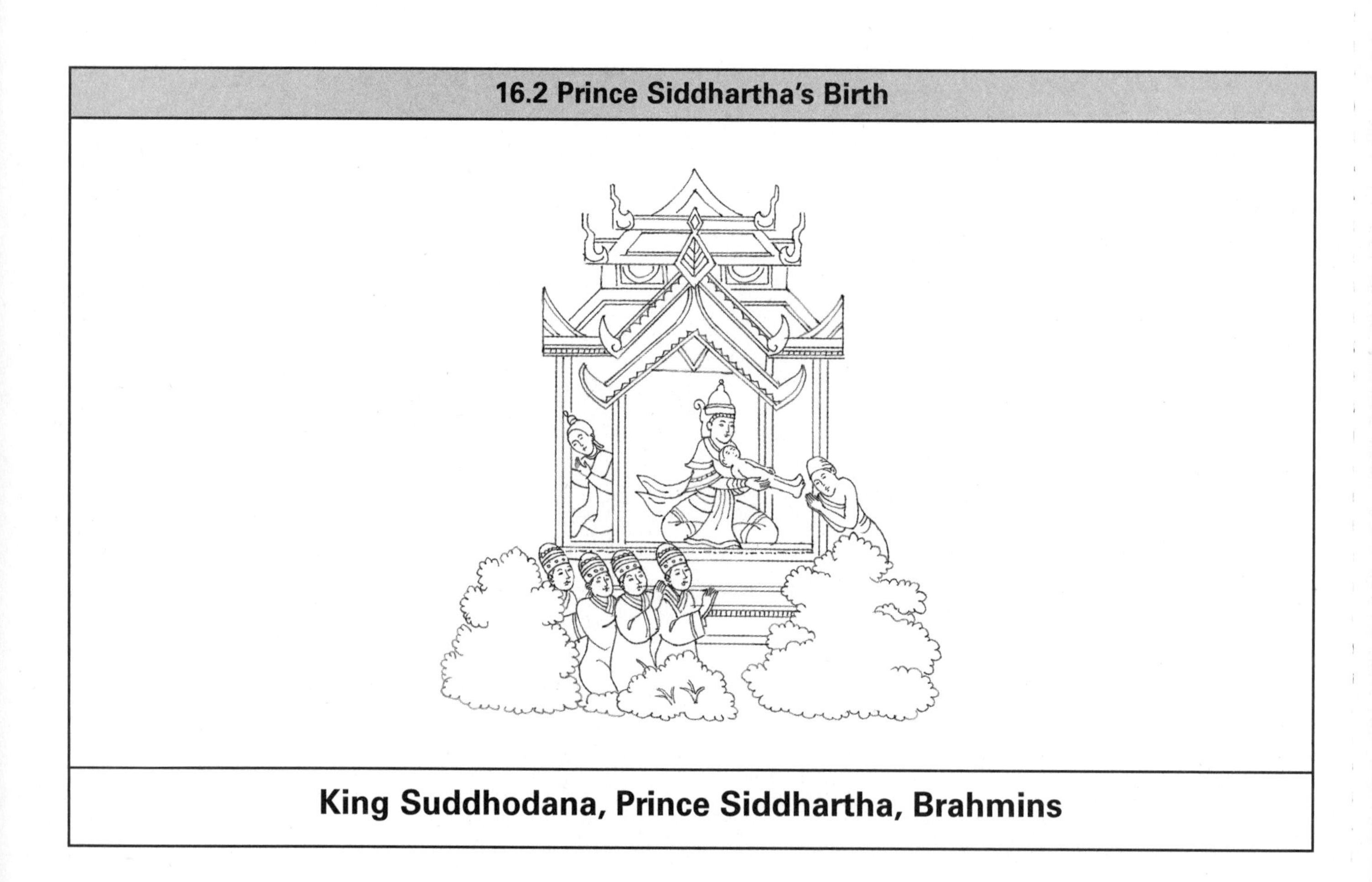

King Suddhodana, Prince Siddhartha, Brahmins

16.3 The Prince's Royal Life

servants, palaces, amusement, wealth

16.4 The Prince Discovers Three Forms of Suffering

ascetic, sickness, death, old age, travel

READING NOTES 16

16.5 The Prince Becomes an Ascetic

forest, bowl, bare feet, simple clothing

16.6 The Prince Becomes the Buddha

the Buddha, Bodhi tree, enlightenment

Write a caption that summarizes each step along Siddhartha's path to enlightenment.

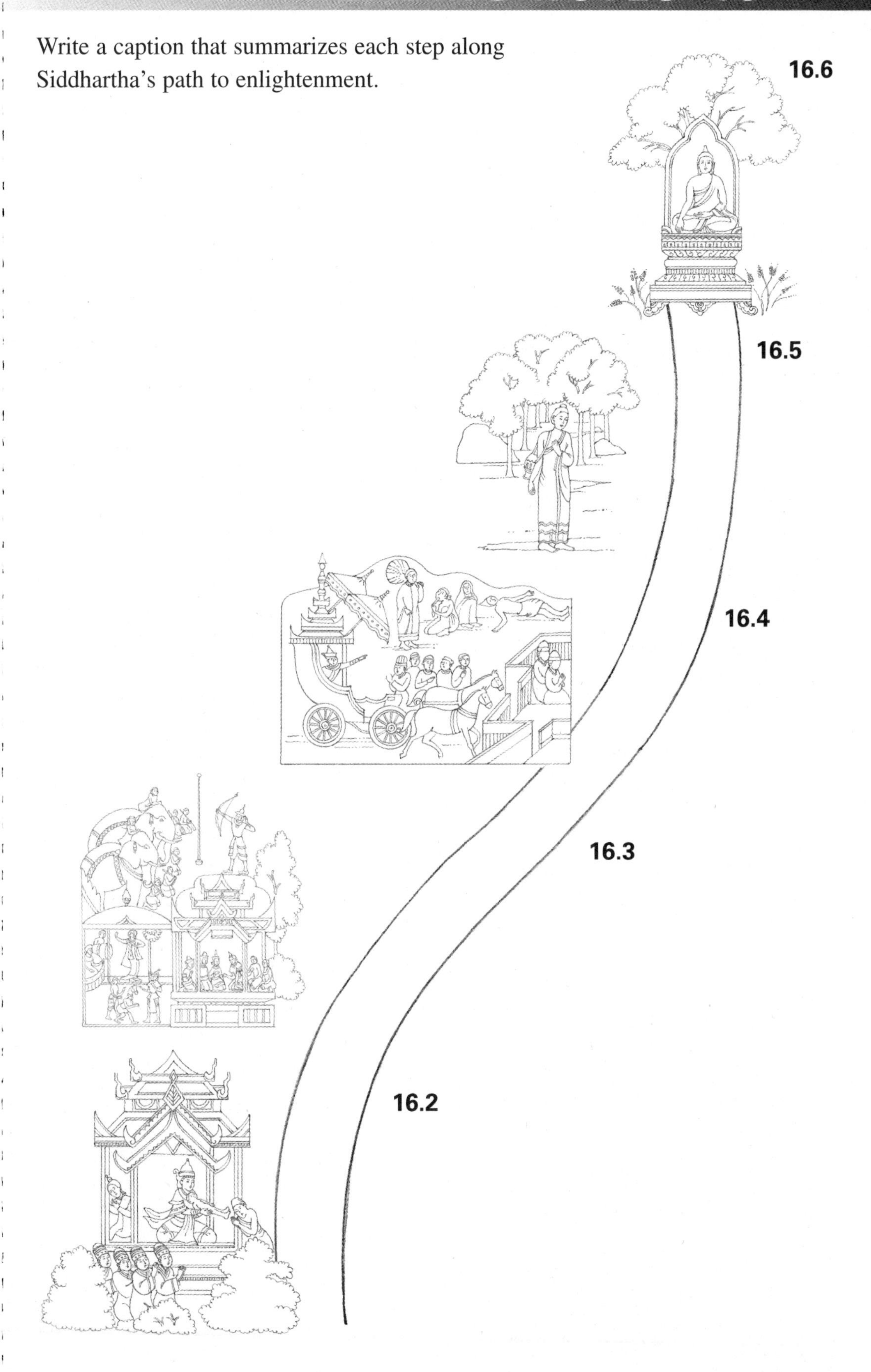

PROCESSING 16

What do you think the Buddha would say is the secret to happiness?

Answer the question by filling in the thought bubble below with words and simple illustrations. Use these words in your response: *wealth, suffering, craving, nirvana.*

PREVIEW 17

Think of the billboards you have seen on the sides of buildings and roadways. There are different kinds of billboards. Some advertise a product. Others promote an idea or cause. All billboards try to change people's behavior.

In the space below, quickly sketch an interesting billboard you have seen.

READING NOTES 17

Read Sections 17.2–17.4. For each section, record notes in the appropriate space.

17.2 The Mauryas Unify India

Shade in the Mauryan Empire on the map.

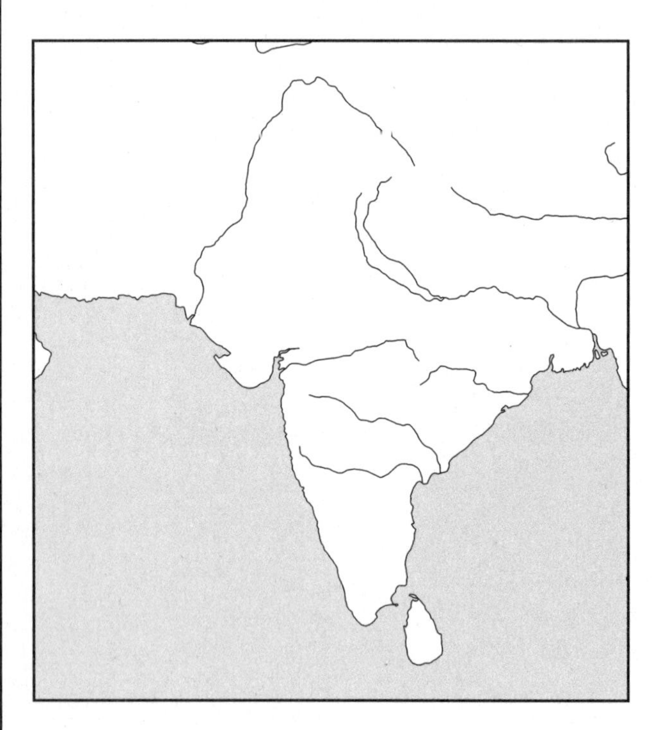

On the pillar, write a paragraph summarizing the expansion of the Mauryan Empire under Chandragupta. Use and underline these words in your summary: *conquer, harsh, unite.*

17.3 Ashoka's Rule	17.4 Ashoka's Edicts
On the pillar, write a paragraph summarizing the expansion of the Mauryan Empire under Ashoka. Use and underline these words in your summary: *conquest, war, Buddhism, change.* 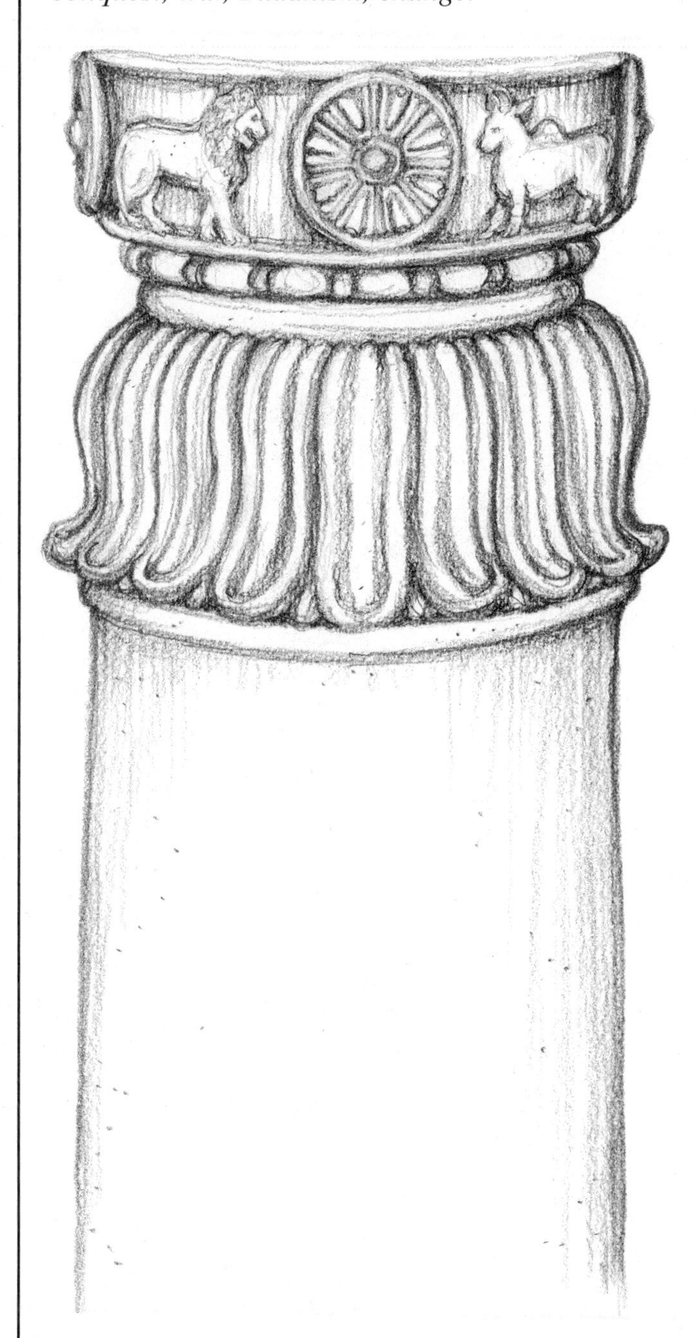	On the pillar, record the four main goals of Ashoka's edicts. 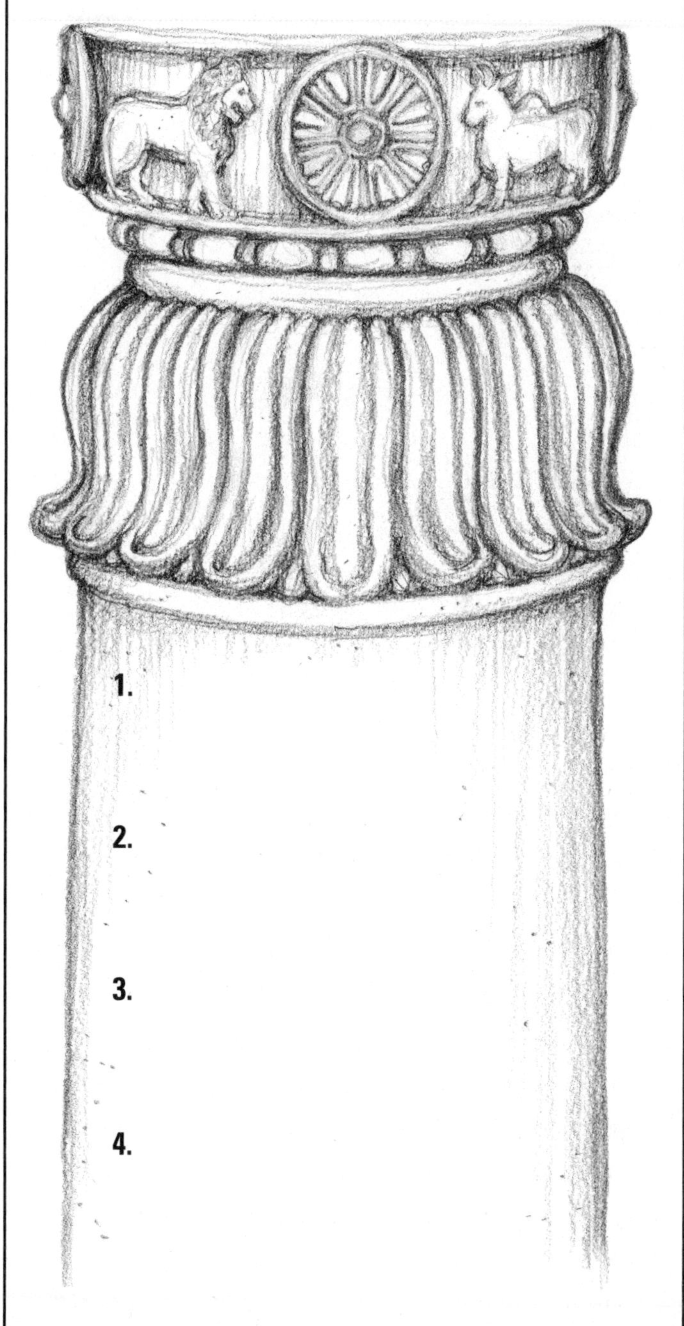 1. 2. 3. 4.

ACTIVITY NOTES 17

Carefully examine Edicts A–I and the billboards posted near them. Circle the goal that you think matches each edict, and explain your choice.

Edict	Goal	Why We Classified Edict Under This Goal
Edict A: "On the roads…trees have been planted for the enjoyment of animals and men. I have had ponds dug and shelters erected along the roads. Everywhere I have had wells dug."	Buddhist values General welfare Justice Security	
Edict B: "It is good to be obedient to one's mother and father, friends, and relatives. It is good not only to spend little, but to own the minimum of property."	Buddhist values General welfare Justice Security	
Edict C: "My officers have been appointed for the welfare [safety] and happiness of the…people. I have given them…authority in judgment and punishment. But it is desirable that there should be uniformity [sameness] in judicial [trial] procedure and punishment."	Buddhist values General welfare Justice Security	
Edict D: "This world and the other [world after death] are hard to gain without great love of righteousness [correct behavior], great self-examination, great obedience, great effort."	Buddhist values General welfare Justice Security	
Edict E: "If the unconquered peoples on my border ask what is my will, they should understand this: I desire that they should trust me and should have only happiness in their dealings with me."	Buddhist values General welfare Justice Security	

Edict	Goal	Why We Classified Edict Under This Goal
Edict F: "This…has been engraved so that the officials of the city should always see to it that no one is ever imprisoned or tortured without good cause. To ensure this I shall send out every five years on a tour of inspection officers who are not fierce or harsh."	Buddhist values General welfare Justice Security	
Edict G: "There is no gift comparable to the gift of dharma [righteousness, or correct behavior], and this is: good behavior toward slaves and servants, obedience to parents, generosity toward friends, acquaintances, and relatives…and abstention [staying away] from killing living beings."	Buddhist values General welfare Justice Security	
Edict H: "Everywhere, I, Ashoka, King Priyadarsi, Beloved of the Gods, have arranged for two kinds of medical treatment: medical treatment for people and medical treatment for animals."	Buddhist values General welfare Justice Security	
Edict I: "Men who are sentenced to death are to be given three days respite [waiting period before being put to death]. Thus their relations may plead for their lives, or the men may make donations or undertake a fast [period of not eating] for a better rebirth in the next life."	Buddhist values General welfare Justice Security	

PROCESSING 17

Like billboards and Ashoka's edicts, Web pages are designed to promote ideas or products. Design a Web page celebrating Ashoka and the Mauryan Empire that includes the following:

- the terms *Chandragupta, Ashoka, Buddhism, edict, empire,* and *dharma.*
- at least four of these features: a Web address, buttons, links, colors, illustrations, or graphics.
- at least one paragraph that describes Ashoka's rule and the Mauryan Empire.

PREVIEW 18

Historians often call a specific time period in a country's history its "golden age." This is usually a time when great accomplishments are made.

Write a short paragraph about a period in your life that you would describe as your golden age. Explain why you chose this period. This might be a time when you were very successful at school, you really enjoyed what you were doing, your sports team was usually winning, or you won an art or a musical competition. It can be any period you are proud of.

READING NOTES 18

Perform the tasks at each station and then complete the palm leaves for Sections 18.3–18.9.

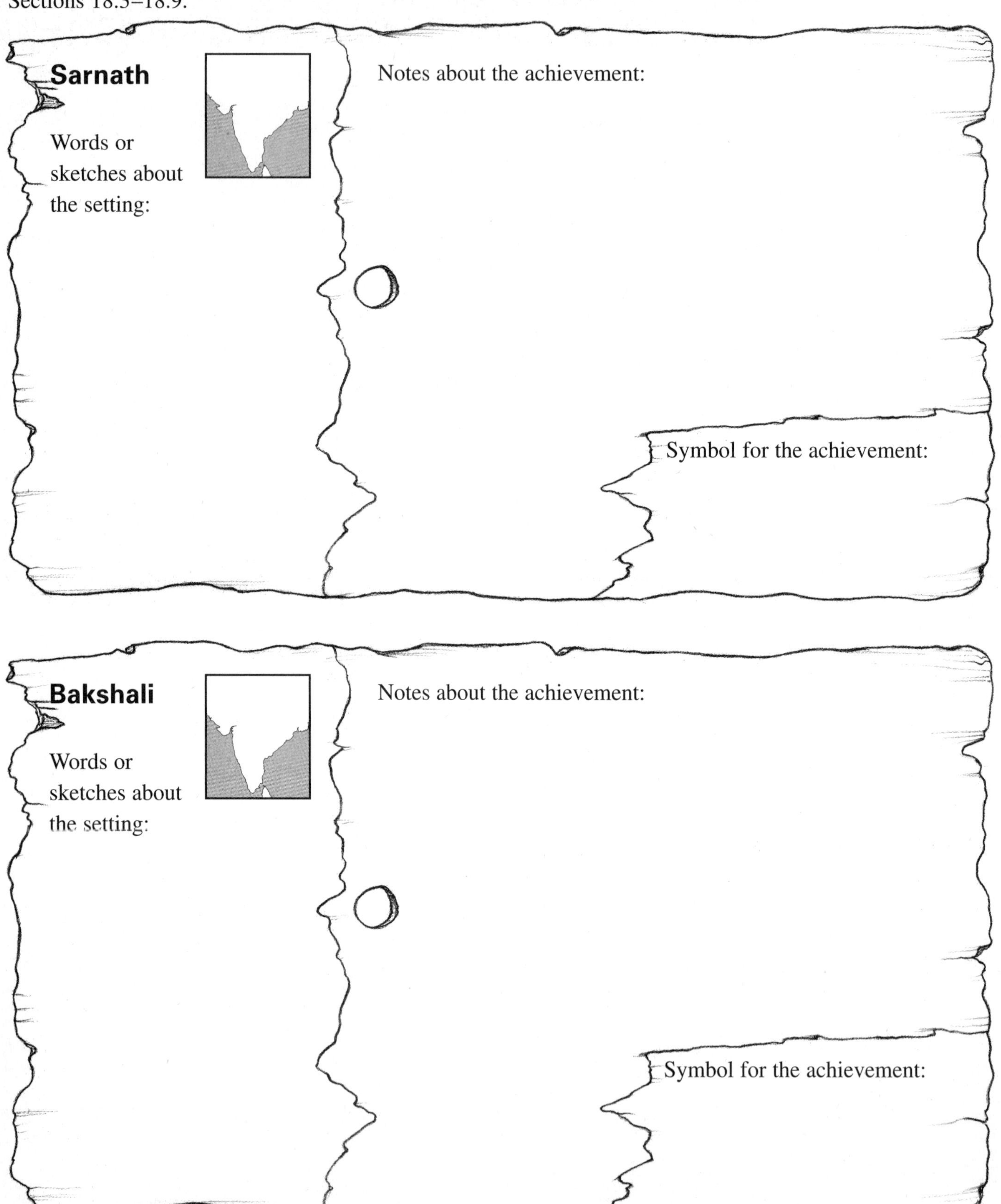

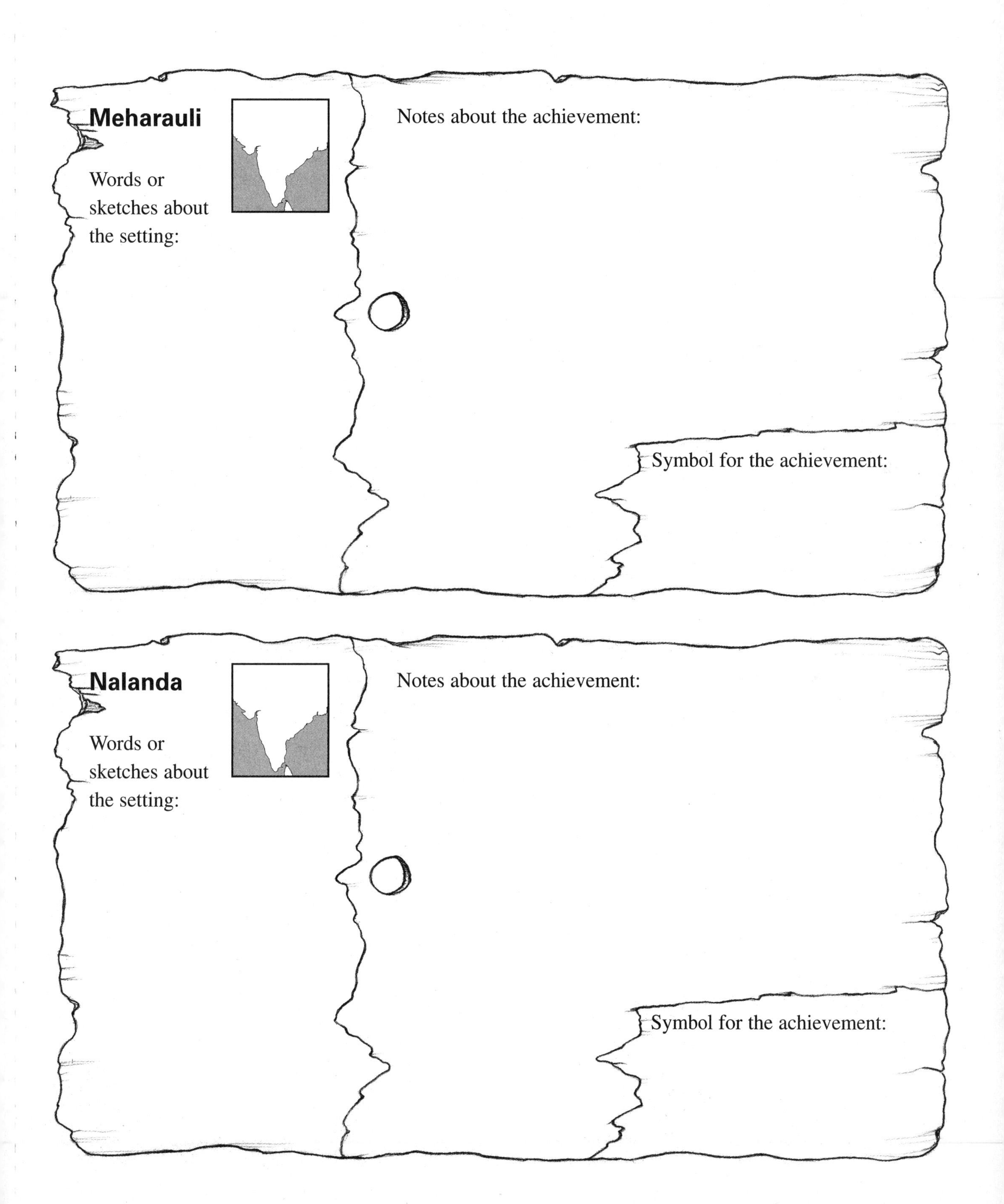
Meharauli
Words or sketches about the setting:
Notes about the achievement:
Symbol for the achievement:
Nalanda
Words or sketches about the setting:
Notes about the achievement:
Symbol for the achievement:

READING NOTES 18

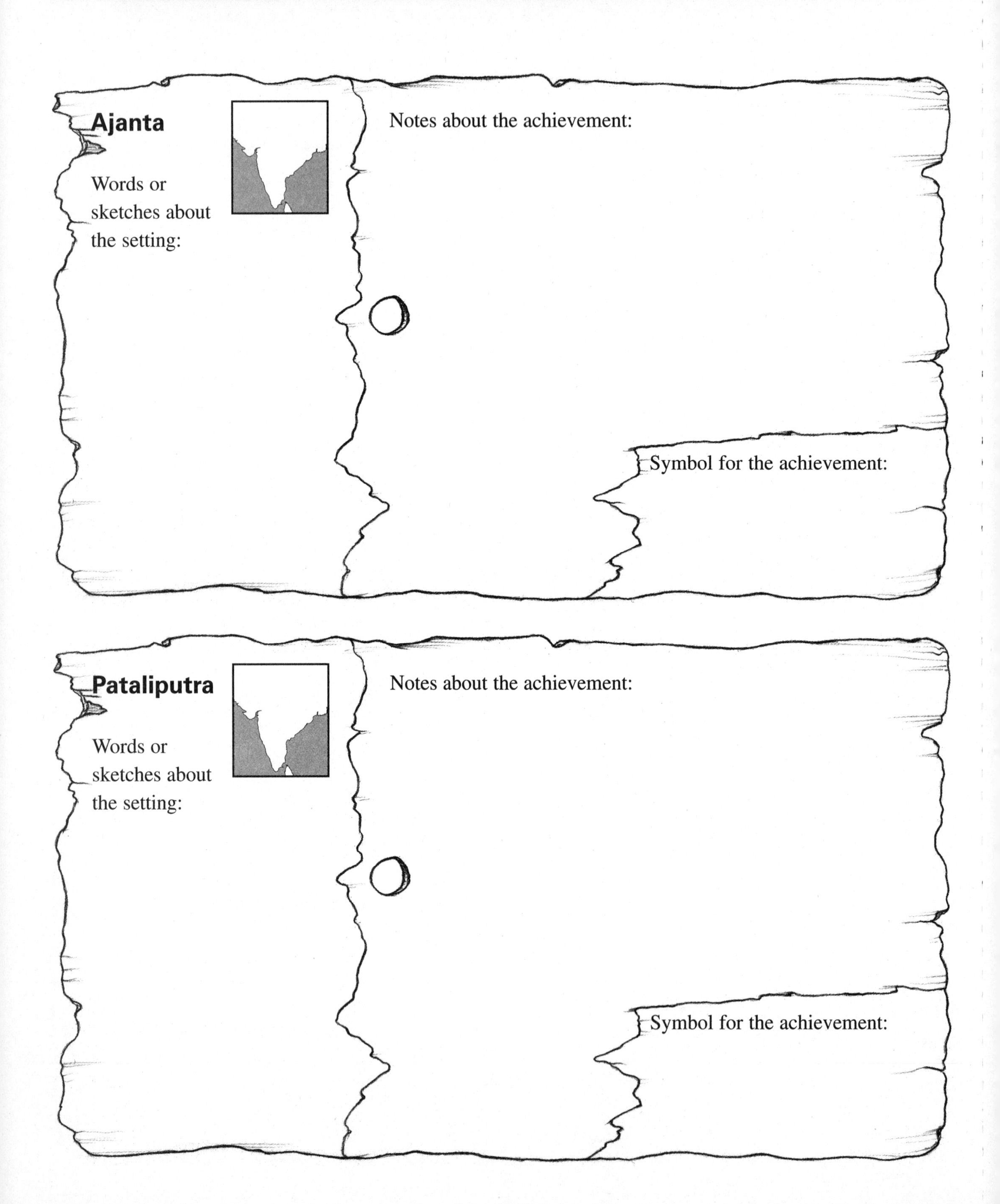

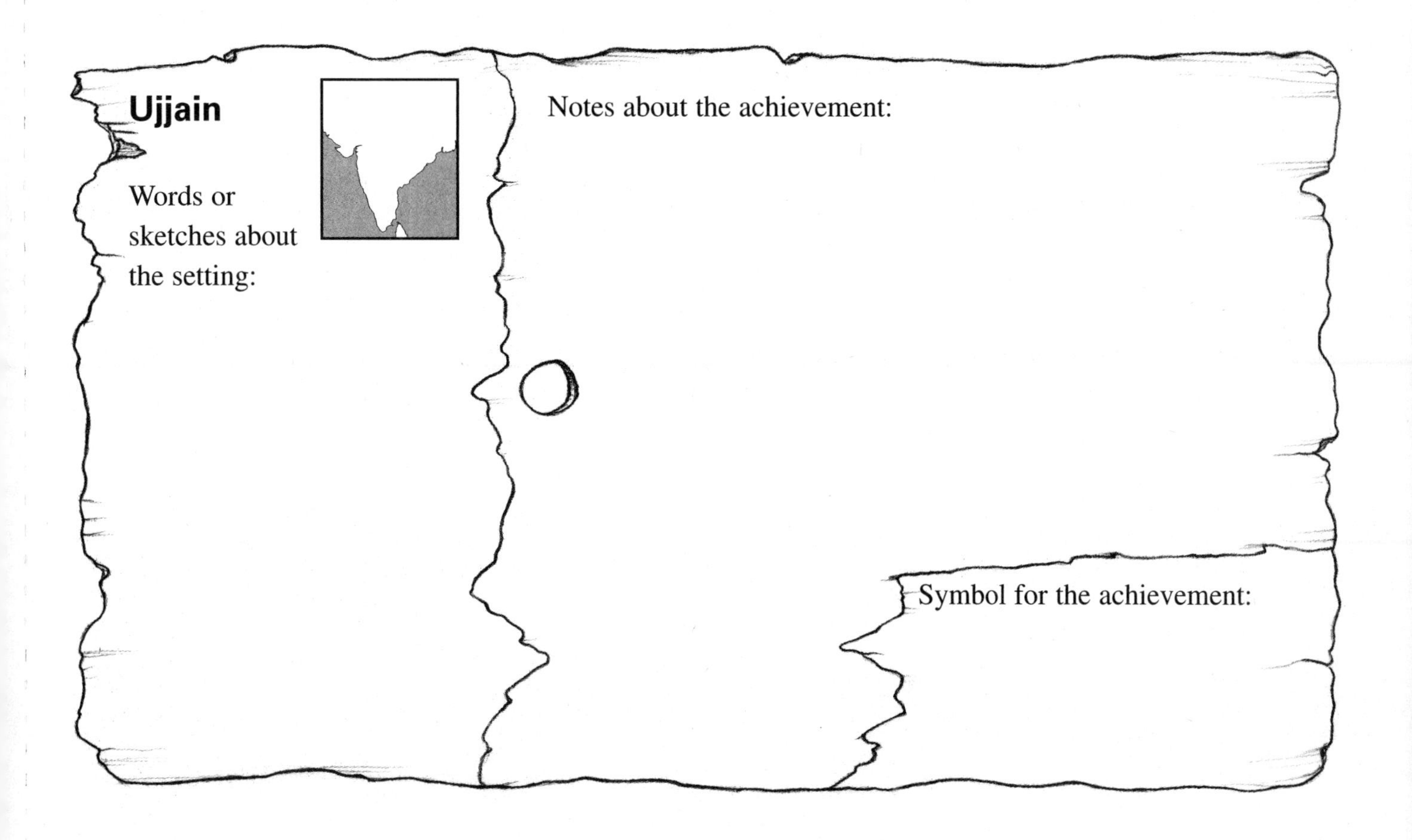
Ujjain
Words or sketches about the setting:
Notes about the achievement:
Symbol for the achievement:

TIMELINE CHALLENGE 3

Use the timeline below to help you complete Items A–F. When completed, each item should include the following:

- the date(s) and a short written description of the item.
- a simple symbol or drawing to represent the item.
- an appropriate geometric shape surrounding the symbol or drawing. The shapes correspond to the categories listed above the right side of the timeline.
- a color bar or dot in the appropriate location on the timeline.
- a line connecting the bar or dot to the geometric shape.

A. 2700 – 1900 B.C.E.
Advanced sewer system is designed in Mohenjodaro.

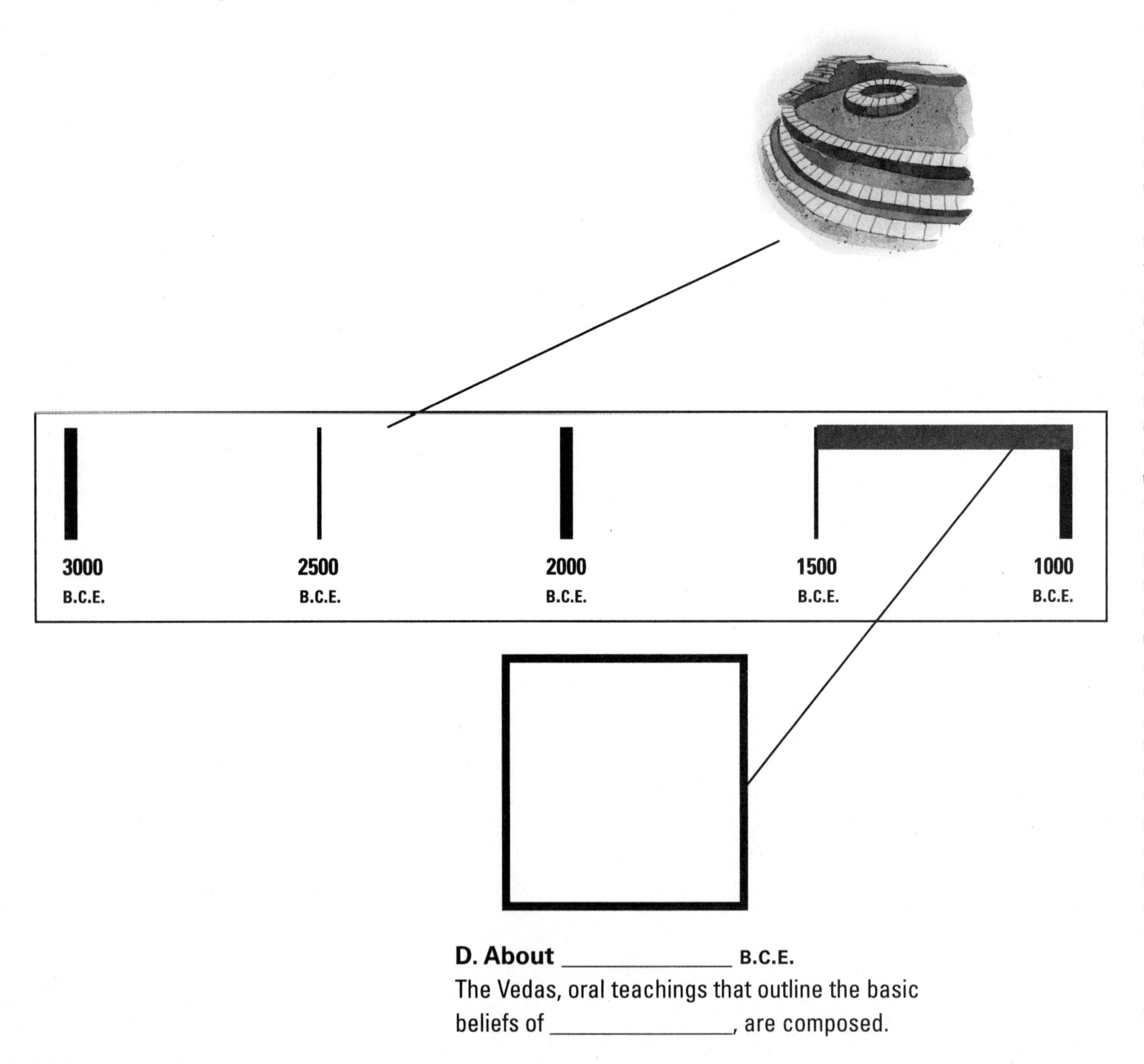

D. About ______________ B.C.E.
The Vedas, oral teachings that outline the basic beliefs of ______________, are composed.

TIMELINE CHALLENGE 3

△ Social Structure ○ Government □ Religion ⬠ Arts ⬡ Technology ▱ Writing System

B. About 500 B.C.E.
Sanskrit language is first written down.

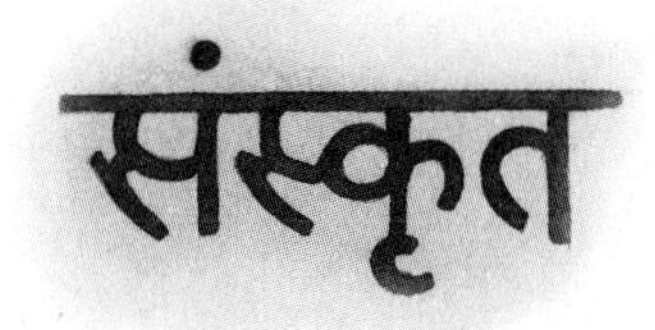

C. 563–483 B.C.E.
Life of Prince Siddhartha, founder of _______________.

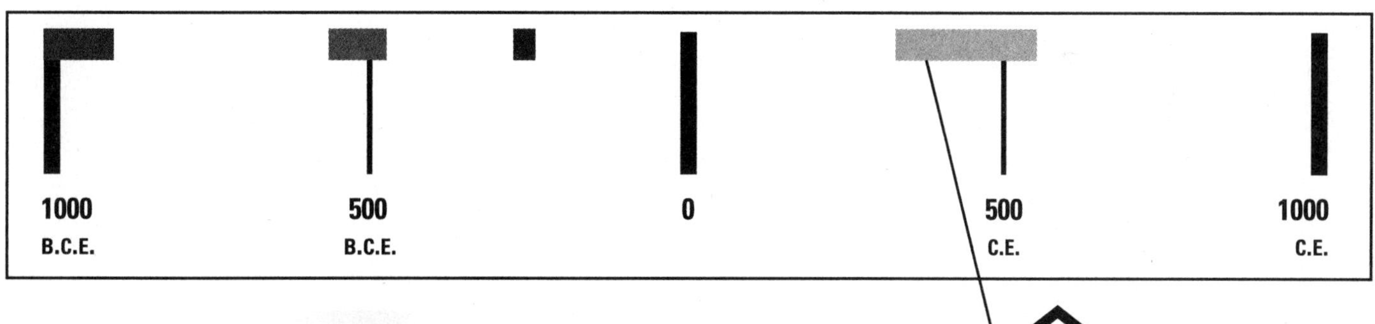

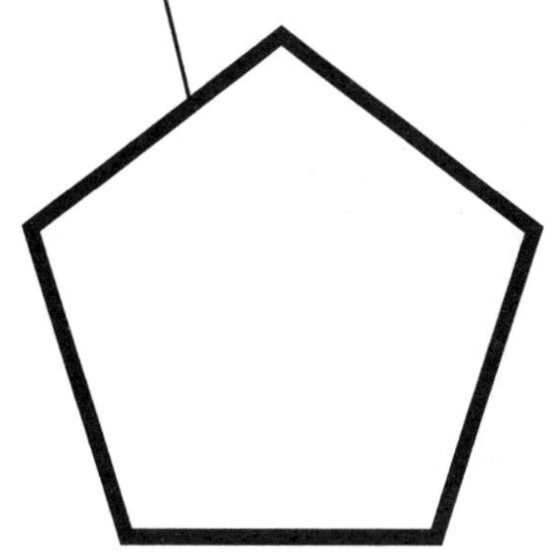

E. 269–232 B.C.E.
Ashoka rules Mauryan Empire using __________ to promote four main goals.

F. _______________ C.E.
Gupta Empire, during which Ajanta cave murals and *Mahabharata* poem are completed.

UNIT 4

Ancient China

GEOGRAPHY CHALLENGE 4

To complete each Geography Challenge card, answer the questions in complete sentences. Label the map on the opposite page as directed.

Question 1 ______________________________

____

Question 2 ______________________________

____

Question 3 ______________________________

____

Question 4 ______________________________

____

Question 5 ______________________________

____

Question 6 ______________________________

____

Question 7 ______________________________

____

Question 8 ______________________________

____

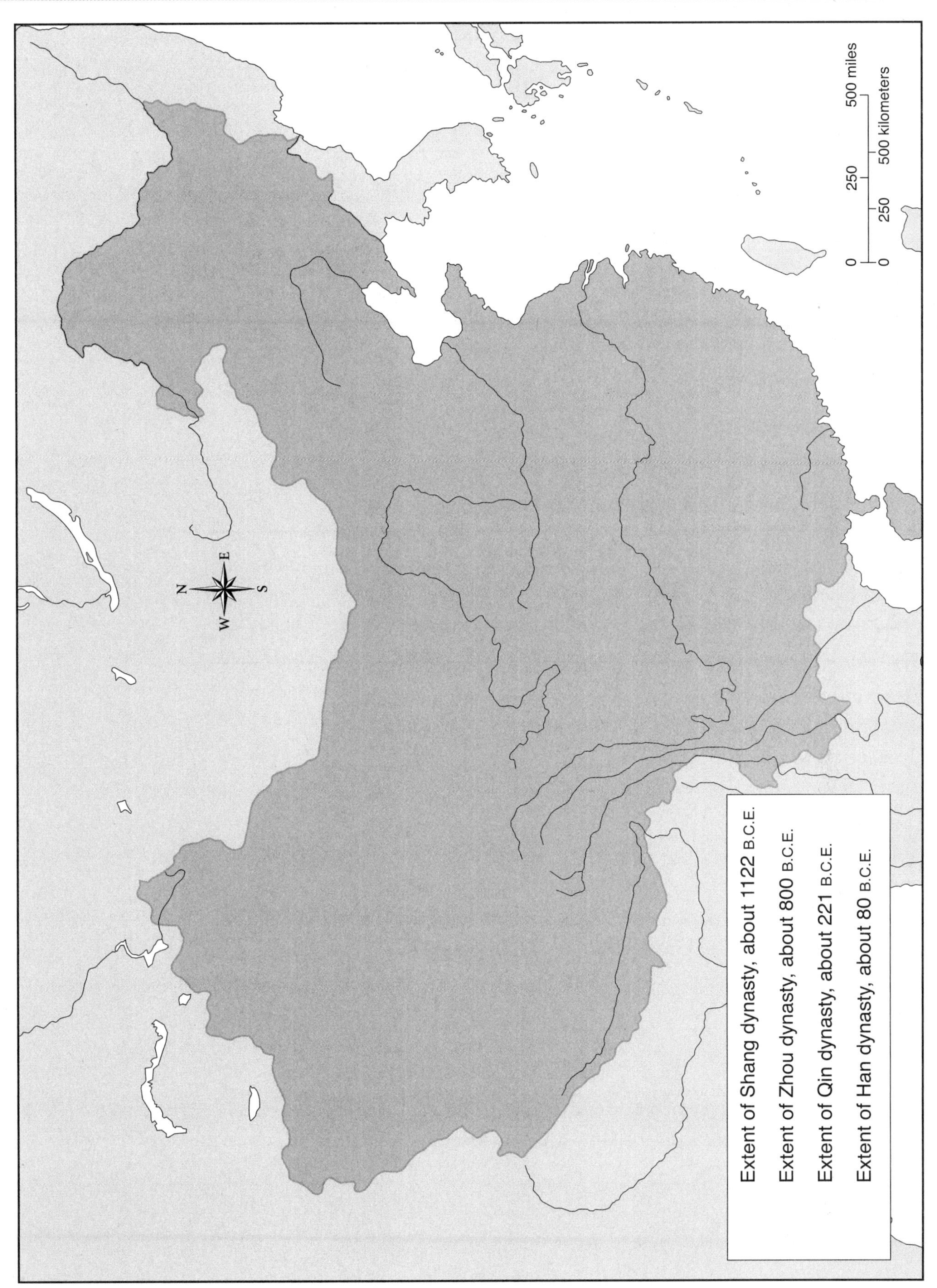
Extent of Shang dynasty, about 1122 B.C.E.
Extent of Zhou dynasty, about 800 B.C.E.
Extent of Qin dynasty, about 221 B.C.E.
Extent of Han dynasty, about 80 B.C.E.
0 250 500 miles
0 250 500 kilometers
N
E
S
W

PREVIEW 19

Answer the questions below about the geography of your community.

Land Features

1. Circle the physical features that are found in your community.

bay	creek	desert	hills	lake	mountains
ocean	plains	plateau	river	valley	coastal plain

2. Land features influence a community. For example, if a community is found near the ocean, a major industry in the community might be fishing. How do land features influence your community?

Climate

1. Circle the words that describe your community's climate.

Summer temperature:	hot	mild	cold
Winter temperature:	hot	mild	cold
Precipitation (rain and snow):	light	moderate	heavy

2. Climate influences a community. For example, if a community has hot summers, houses often have air-conditioning. How does climate influence your community?

Vegetation

1. What natural vegetation do you have in your community? For example, does your community have grasslands, forests, scrub vegetation, or no vegetation?

2. Vegetation influences a community. For example, a community with forests may have a lumber industry. How does the natural vegetation influence your community?

READING NOTES 19

Part 1: Read the hypothesis. Using only your poster with the relief map, give four reasons that support this hypothesis. (**Hint:** Include reasons why some other regions would not be good for settlement.)

Hypothesis 1: Most early people settled on the North China Plain because of its geography.

These four reasons support this hypothesis:

1.

2.

3.

4.

Part 2

1. Read Section 19.8. Add any additional information that shows that most early people settled on the North China Plain because of its geography.

2. On the map, draw in and label the Huang He. Color the North China Plain the color of the soil found there.

Taklimakan Desert
Gobi Desert
Northeastern Plain
North China Plain
Tibet-Qinghai Plateau
Chang Jiang Basins

READING NOTES 19

Part 1: Read the hypothesis. Using only your poster with the relief map, give two reasons that support this hypothesis.

Hypothesis 2: China was isolated from other civilizations because of its geography.

These two reasons support this hypothesis:

1.

2.

Part 2

1. Read Section 19.9. Add any additional information that shows China was isolated from other civilizations because of its geography.

2. On the map, color the areas that caused China to be isolated from other civilizations.

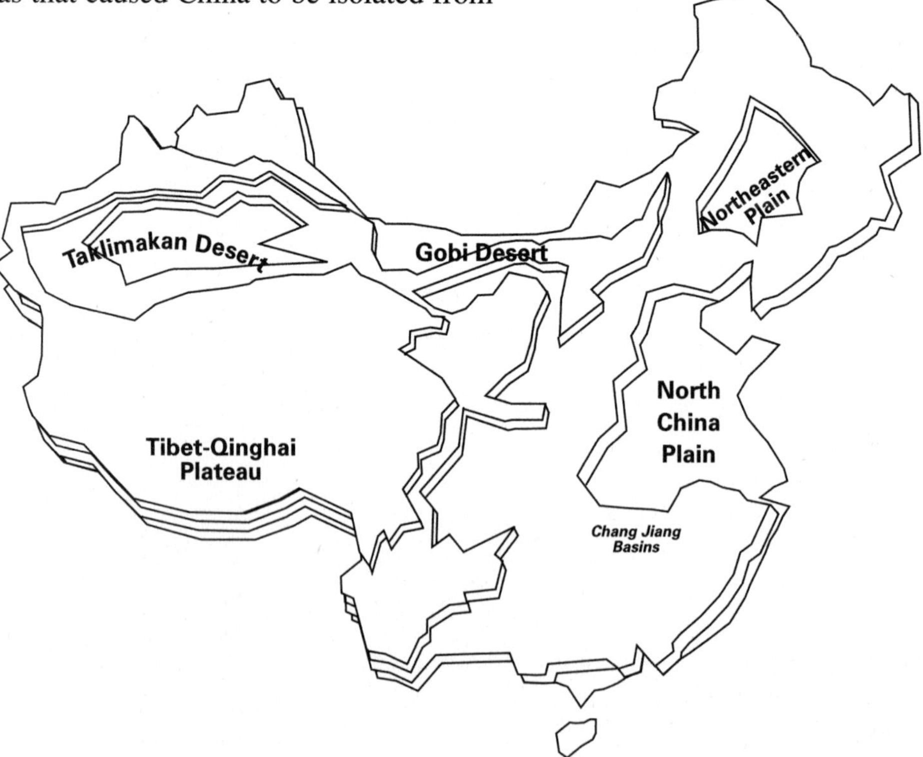

READING NOTES 19

Part 1: Read the hypothesis. Using only your poster with the relief map, give five reasons that support this hypothesis. (**Hint:** Think about physical features, climate, and vegetation in each geographic region. What differences might result in how people lived, what they ate, or what kinds of shelter they used?)

Hypothesis 3: Because of geography, several ways of life developed in China.

These five reasons support this hypothesis:

1.

2.

3.

4.

5.

Part 2

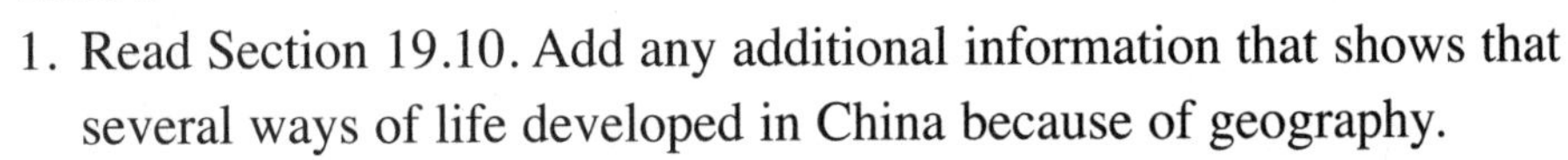

1. Read Section 19.10. Add any additional information that shows that several ways of life developed in China because of geography.

2. In each box, draw one type of food, shelter, *or* activity (such as farming or herding animals) that might be found in that geographic region.

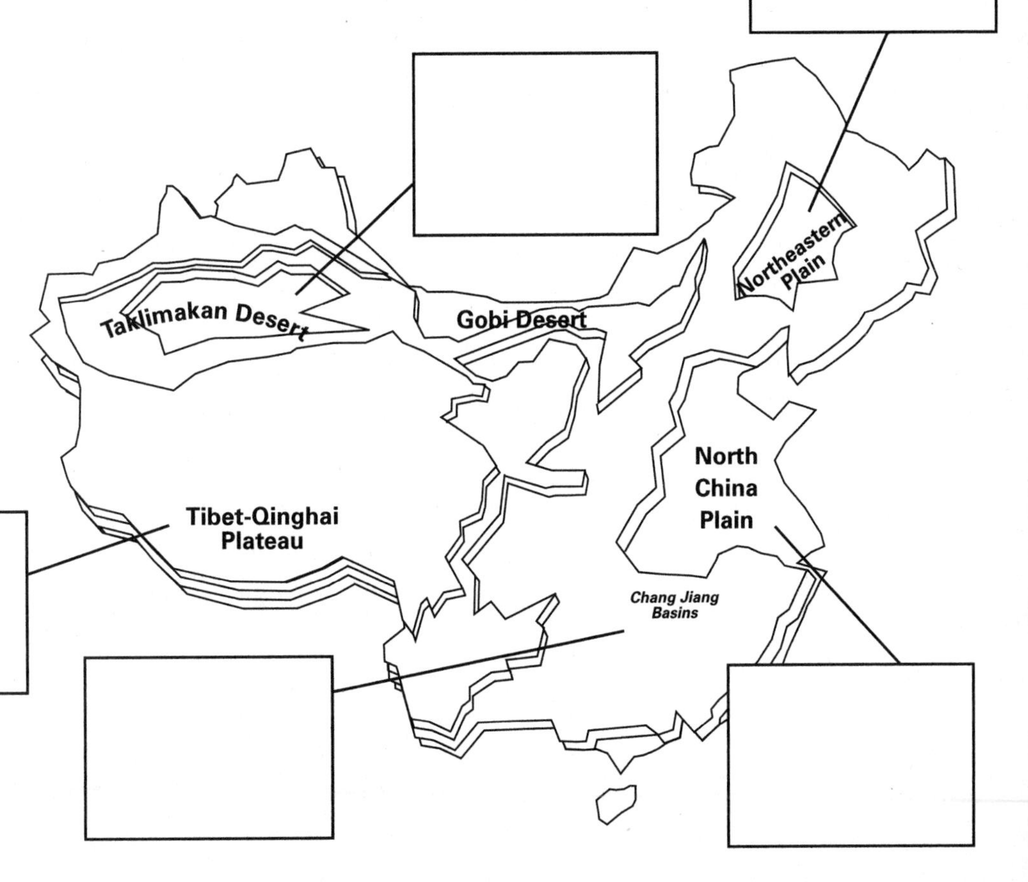

PROCESSING 19

The Chinese often drew pictures of the landscape on scrolls. Choose two of China's geographic regions, and illustrate the geography and way of life in each region. Your scroll might show these things:

- physical features (such as mountains and rivers), climate, and vegetation
- clothing, food, or shelter of people living in that region

Use at least four colors. Below your scroll, write a paragraph that compares and contrasts the two regions.

PREVIEW 20

Imagine that you are an archeologist in 3000 C.E. You have recently unearthed several artifacts. Each artifact tells you about one characteristic of the civilization of the United States.

In the chart, write something that each artifact indicates about that characteristic. For example, if you found a crown, you might write, "This civilization was probably governed by a king or a queen."

Characteristic of the Civilization	Artifact	What This Artifact Reveals
Government	BALLOT BOX	
Social Structure		
Religion		
Writing	History Alive!	
Art		
Technology		

READING NOTES 20

Follow these steps to excavate artifacts from the Shang tomb:

1. Excavate an artifact, and retrieve a matching decoder.
2. Answer the questions on the artifact. Check your answers with the decoder.
3. In the table, record the secret word and the reading section number shown on the decoder.

Artifact	Secret Word	Section Number	Two Important Facts About the Shang Dynasty	Other Characteristics of the Shang Dynasty This Artifact Reveals					
				Government	Social Structure	Religion	Writing	Art	Technology
A									
B									
C									
D									

4. Read that section of your book. In the table, record two important facts you learn.
5. In the table, check other characteristics of the Shang civilization that this artifact reveals. You may check more than one.

Artifact	Secret Word	Section Number	Two Important Facts About the Shang Dynasty	Other Characteristics of the Shang Dynasty This Artifact Reveals					
				Government	Social Structure	Religion	Writing	Art	Technology
E									
F									
G									
H									

PROCESSING 20

Decorate the bronze vessel below by drawing two artifacts from the Shang tomb. Each artifact should reveal information about two or more characteristics of the Shang dynasty. Beneath the vessel, write a paragraph explaining what each artifact tells us about the Shang dynasty.

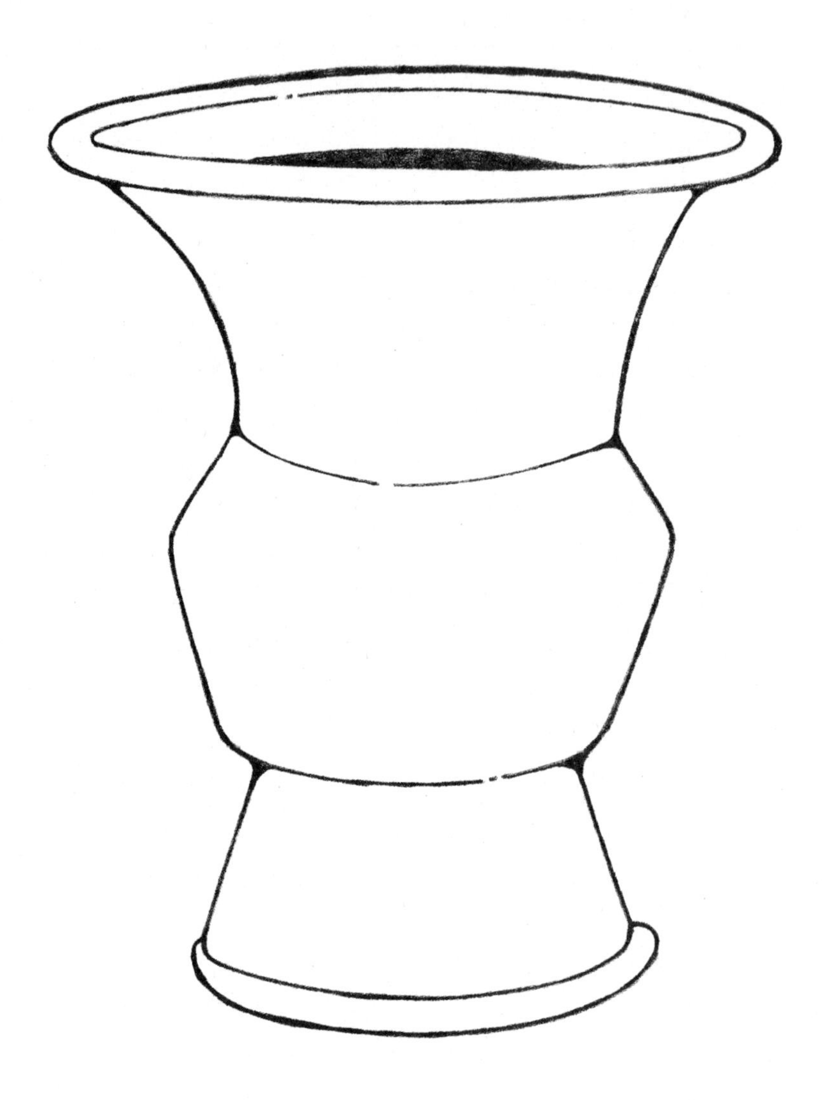

PREVIEW 21

Which of the following approaches do you think would be most effective in dealing with school violence such as fighting and bullying? Write a paragraph that explains your answer.

- *Approach 1:* Assign students who are guilty of violent behavior around the school a "big brother" or "big sister" who is a respected older student from another grade. The big brother or sister would teach the student how to behave properly.
- *Approach 2:* Allow students who are guilty of fighting or bullying to go unpunished, hoping that eventually they will learn from their mistakes and correct their behavior.
- *Approach 3:* Have school authorities put in writing rules about unacceptable behavior and assign harsh punishments for violating the rules. For example, students caught fighting will be expelled.

21.2 The Zhou Dynasty

Answer the questions below.

1. What was the Mandate of Heaven?

2. What is feudalism?

21.3 Confucianism

In accordance with Confucian traditions, obey and respect your elder by answering the questions correctly.

1. Who was Confucius?

2. What was China like during his life?

3. According to Confucius, what are the five basic relationships?

4. How should people act in the basic relationships?

5. What influence did Confucius have on Chinese government?

6. Write a caption for the image that would make your elder proud.

21.4 Daoism

In accordance with Daoist traditions, demonstrate that you understand the following ideas of Daoism in any way you want.

1. Who was Laozi?

2. According to Daoism, how should people discover how to behave?

3. What are yin and yang?

4. According to Daoists, how should rulers behave?

5. If you want to, write a caption for the image.

21.5 Legalism

Answer the questions below. In accordance with Legalist traditions, you will be "punished" for incorrect answers.

1. Who was Hanfeizi?

2. According to Hanfeizi, what was the only way to create a strong society?

3. How did Hanfeizi believe a ruler should govern?

4. How did the Qin dynasty apply the teachings of Hanfeizi?

5. Write a caption for the image right now!

PROCESSING 21

Complete each step.

1. Describe your family's policy about your homework. For example, do you have a special place to work? Can you listen to music or watch TV? Does someone help you? Are there consequences for failing to do your homework?

2. Which of the following schools of thought is your family's policy toward your doing your homework most like? Circle one.

   Confucianism **Daoism** **Legalism**

   Explain your answer.

3. Explain Confucianism, Daoism, and Legalism to your parent or guardian.

4. Ask your parent or guardian to decide whether the family policy toward homework is most like the practices of Confucianism, Daoism, or Legalism. Write your parent's or guardian's answer here.

5. Discuss with your parent or guardian the answers to Question 2 and Question 4. Do your answers agree? If not, talk about why your answers differ.

____

Signature of parent or guardian

PREVIEW 22

Think about a friend you have. Rate how effective this person is as a friend by marking an X on the spectrum for each characteristic listed. Do not mention your friend's name.

Characteristic	Never	Sometimes	Always
1. Can keep a secret			
2. Follows through on promises			
3. Listens to me			
4. Is loyal			
5. Helps me when I need help			
6. Remembers my birthday			
7. Accepts my faults			
8. Trusts me			

22.2 Creating an Empire

Step 1: Look at the projected image. Label five details in it by drawing a line to each detail below and labeling it.

Step 2: Read Section 22.2. Answer the questions below.

1. Do you think Qin Shihuangdi's strategy of conquest helped or hurt China? Explain your answer.

2. How did Qin Shihuangdi end feudalism? Why did he do this?

Step 3: Did the Emperor of Qin's efforts to unite China make him an effective ruler? Mark your answer with an X on the spectrum below.

Very Ineffective — Very Effective

22.3 Standardizing the Culture

Step 1: Look at the projected image. Label five details in it by drawing a line to each detail below and labeling it.

Step 2: Read Section 22.3. Answer the questions below.

1. Why did the Emperor of Qin standardize money, weights, and measures?

2. How did the Emperor of Qin change the written language?

Step 3: Did the Emperor of Qin's efforts to standardize Chinese culture make him an effective ruler? Mark your answer with an X on the spectrum below.

Very Ineffective — Very Effective

22.4 Protecting the Northern Border

Step 1: Look at the projected image. Label five details in it by drawing a line to each detail below and labeling it.

Step 2: Read Section 22.4.
Answer the questions below.

1. How did the emperor protect China's northern border?

2. What difficulties did workers who constructed the Great Wall face?

Step 3: Did the Emperor of Qin's efforts to protect China's northern border make him an effective ruler? Mark your answer with an X on the spectrum below.

Very Ineffective | Very Effective

22.5 Ending Opposition

Step 1: Look at the projected image. Label five details in it by drawing a line to each detail below and labeling it.

Step 2: Read Section 22.5. Answer the questions below.

1. Why was there a conflict between Confucian scholars and the emperor?

2. What did the emperor do to prevent people from learning about Confucianism?

Step 3: Did the Emperor of Qin's efforts to end opposition make him an effective ruler? Mark your answer with an X on the spectrum below.

Very Ineffective | Very Effective

22.6 The Emperor's Death and the End of the Qin Dynasty

Step 1: Look at the projected image. Label five details in it by drawing a line to each detail below and labeling it.

Step 2: Read Section 22.6 Answer the questions below.

1. List three things that were buried in the Emperor of Qin's tomb.

2. What happened to the Qin dynasty after the death of Qin Shihuangdi?

Step 3: Did the Emperor of Qin's efforts to become immortal make him an effective ruler? Mark your answer with an X on the spectrum below.

Very Ineffective | Very Effective

PROCESSING 22

Decide whether Qin Shihuangdi was an effective or an ineffective ruler. If you believe he was an effective ruler, design a commemorative plaque in the space below. If you believe he was an ineffective ruler, design a "wanted" poster in the space below. Your plaque or poster must contain the following:

- a title that indicates whether it is a commemorative plaque or a "wanted" poster
- a picture of the emperor
- at least three actions of the emperor that justify this plaque or poster, with illustrations for each action

Choose one of the most important achievements you have made in your life. This might be an academic, artistic, athletic, or social achievement. For example, you might have made the honor roll for the first time, organized a musical group or learned to play a musical instrument, been chosen for a sports team, or helped someone in need.

Describe the event below. Then tell who was affected in a positive way by your achievement. Perhaps your parents were pleased, your team improved, or someone was helped by your achievement.

READING NOTES 23

Station A: Warfare

Step 1: Read and guess the answer to the question on Placard 23A.

Your guess: _____ Correct answer: _____

Step 2: Read Section 23.2 and answer these questions:

1. How far did the Han empire extend?

2. What weapons made the Han army strong?

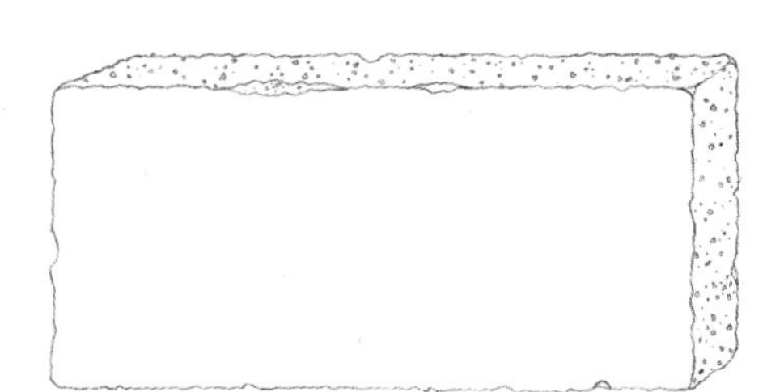

3. On the tomb brick, quickly sketch and label a new weapon that strengthened the Han army.

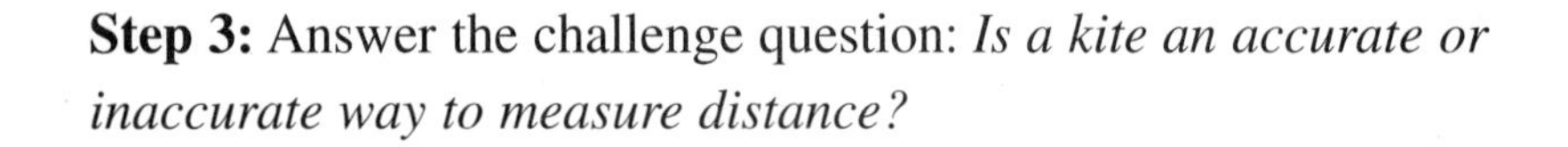

Step 3: Answer the challenge question: *Is a kite an accurate or inaccurate way to measure distance?*

Station B: Government

Step 1: Read and guess the answer to the question on Placard 23B.

Your guess: _____ Correct answer: _____

Step 2: Read Section 23.3 and answer these questions:

1. What is a bureaucracy?

2. How did Han emperors decide who would receive government jobs?

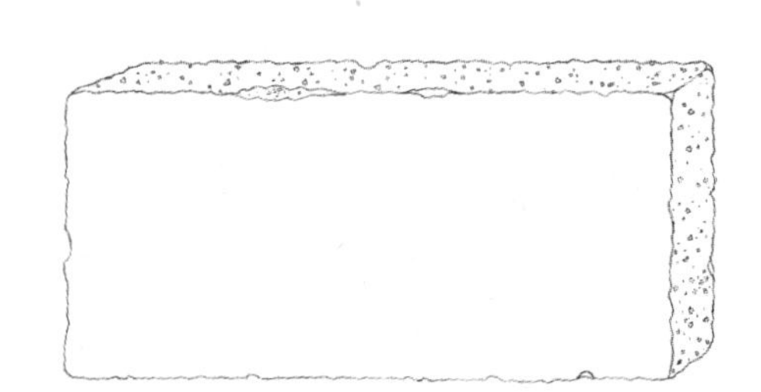

3. On the tomb brick, quickly sketch and label a picture that shows how Han emperors chose government officials.

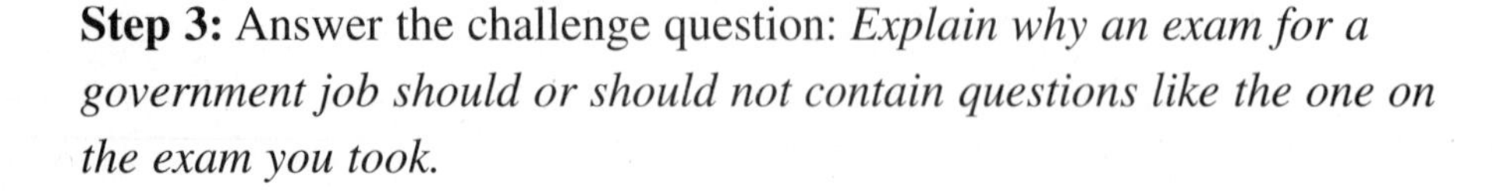

Step 3: Answer the challenge question: *Explain why an exam for a government job should or should not contain questions like the one on the exam you took.*

Station C: Agriculture

Step 1: Read and guess the answer to the question on Placard 23C.

Your guess: _____ Correct answer: _____

Step 2: Read Section 23.4 and answer these questions:

1. What problems did farmers face during the Han period?

2. Explain how the tools that were developed during the Han period helped farmers.

3. On the tomb brick, quickly sketch a new tool that helped farmers during the Han period.

Step 3: Answer the challenge question: *Why do you think the design of the wheelbarrow was changed from ancient to modern times?*

Station D: Industry

Step 1: Read and guess the answer to the question on Placard 23D.

Your guess: _____ Correct answer: _____

Step 2: Read Section 23.5 and answer these questions:

1. How was the production of silk made easier during the Han period?

2. How did the Chinese make it easier to get salt during the Han period?

3. On the tomb brick, quickly sketch and label an invention that helped industry.

Step 3: Answer the challenge question: *What parts of the Chinese drilling process do the glass of water, the straw, and the empty glass represent?*

READING NOTES 23

Station E: Art

Step 1: Read and guess the answer to the question on Placard 23E.

Your guess: _____ Correct answer: _____

Step 2: Read Section 23.6 and answer these questions:

1. What type of writing materials did the Chinese use before the invention of paper?

2. Why was paper an improvement over other writing materials?

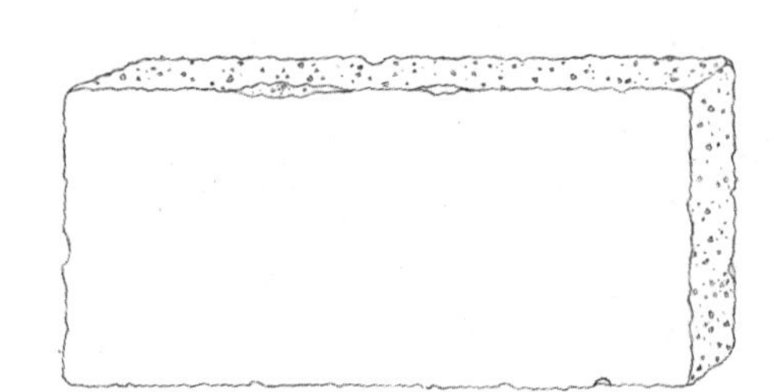

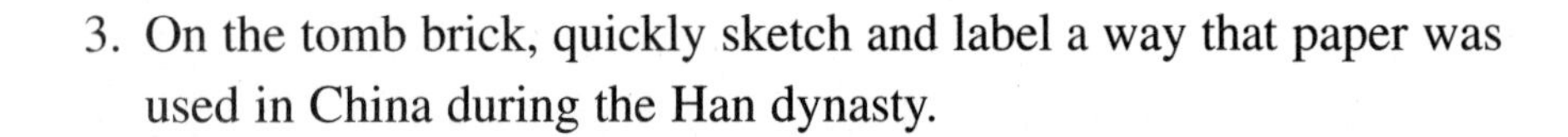

3. On the tomb brick, quickly sketch and label a way that paper was used in China during the Han dynasty.

Step 3: Answer the challenge question: *Why did your character turn out better than if you had used silk or a strip of bamboo instead of paper?*

Station F: Medicine

Step 1: Read and guess the answer to the question on Placard 23F.

Your guess: _____ Correct answer: _____

Step 2: Read Section 23.7 and answer these questions:

1. What is moxibustion?

2. What did the Chinese discover about blood?

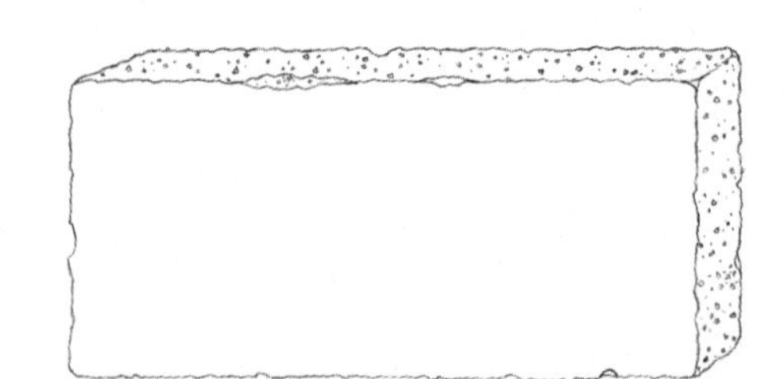

3. On the tomb brick, quickly sketch and label an achievement of the Chinese in the field of health during the Han period.

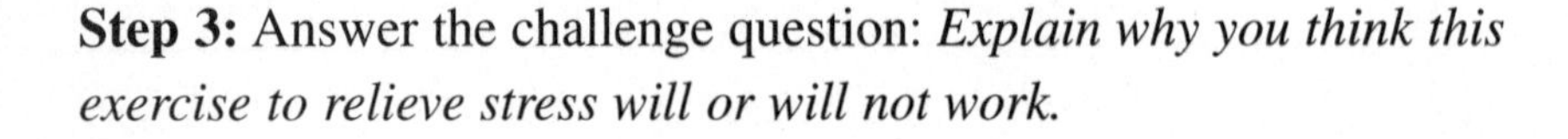

Step 3: Answer the challenge question: *Explain why you think this exercise to relieve stress will or will not work.*

Station G: Science

Step 1: Read and guess the answer to the question on Placard 23G.

Your guess: _____ Correct answer: _____

Step 2: Read Section 23.8 and answer these questions:

1. What did Chinese astronomers discover?

2. For what purpose were the first compasses used?

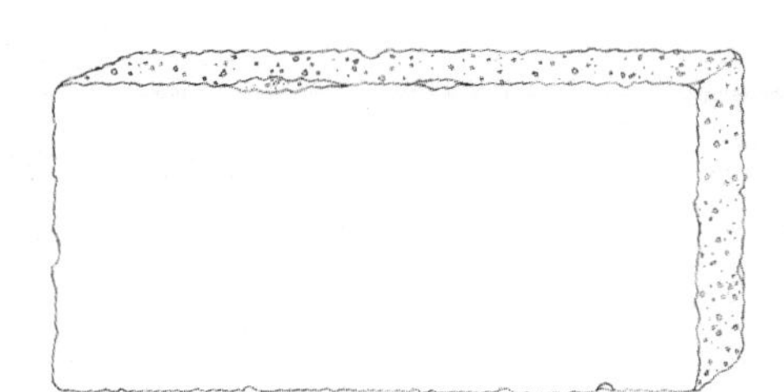

3. On the tomb brick, quickly sketch and label a scientific instrument that helped the Han emperors.

Step 3: Answer the challenge question: *A modern seismograph can give more information than ancient Chinese seismographs. Give an example of this additional information.*

PROCESSING 23

If you were living in China at the time of the Han dynasty, which of the achievements you learned about would you believe had the greatest effect on people's lives? For example, you might think that the chain pump was most important because it allowed fields to be more easily irrigated and, therefore, improved food production.

Draw an illustration of the achievement you choose on the brick below. Color your illustration, using at least four colors.

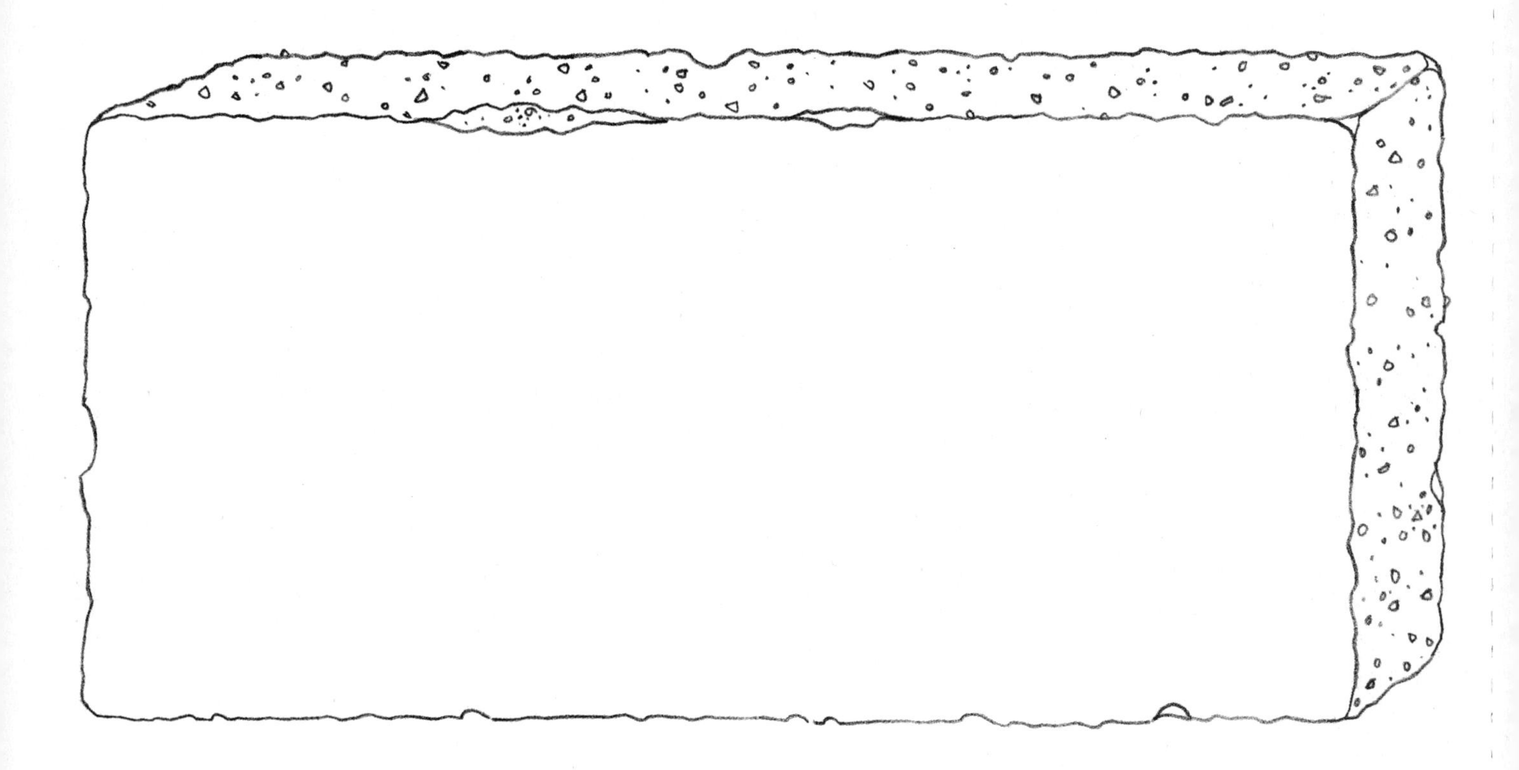

Write a short paragraph that explains why you chose the achievement you did.

READING NOTES 24

Read each section and answer the questions.

24.3 Rome Trades Glassware for Silk

1. How did the Romans first learn about silk?

2. What product could the Romans trade that was unknown to the Chinese?

24.5 The Western Silk Road

1. List two dangers of traveling the western part of the Silk Road.

2. List two products from Egypt, Arabia, and Persia traded on the Silk Road.

3. Why did the Roman emperor stop men from wearing silk?

24.4 The Eastern Silk Road

1. List two dangers of traveling the eastern part of the Silk Road.

2. List two products China sent to the West.

3. List three products Central Asia traded on the Silk Road.

4. List three products from India that were traded on the Silk Road.

24.2 The Opening of the Silk Road

1. List three things Zhang Qian brought back to China after his journey to Central Asia.

2. What product could China trade that was unknown to the West?

24.6 Cultural Exchanges Along the Silk Road

1. List three plants that China learned about as a result of trade on the Silk Road.

2. List three plants the West learned about as a result of trade on the Silk Road.

3. What new religion entered China by way of the Silk Road?

PROCESSING 24

Complete the game board of the Silk Road. In four squares, write four dangers that traders faced on the Silk Road and the number of spaces a player must move back for meeting each danger.

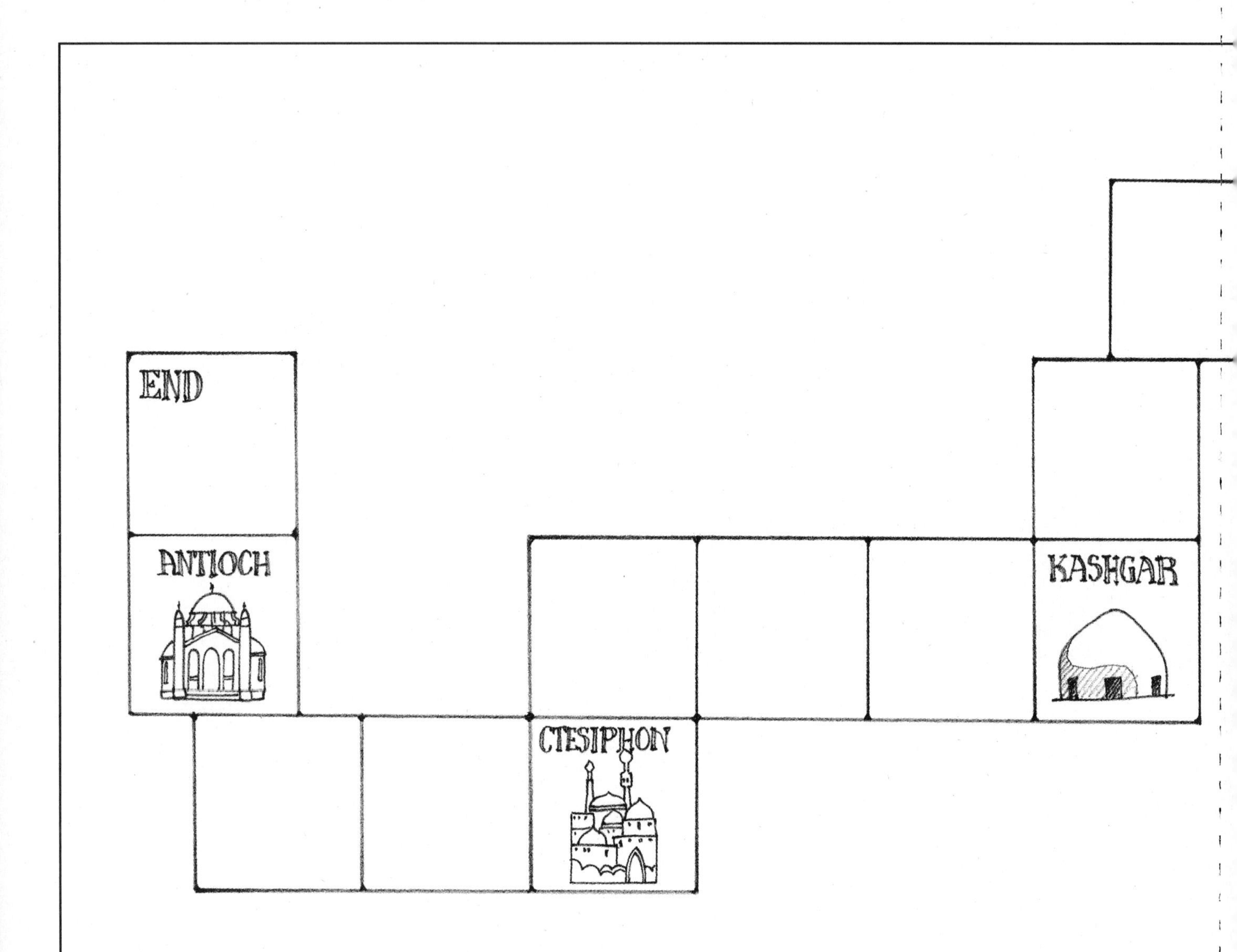

SILK ROAD GAME

PROCESSING 24

In four other squares, write four positive things that could happen to traders on the Silk Road and the number of spaces a trader can move forward. Add decorations and illustrations to your game board.

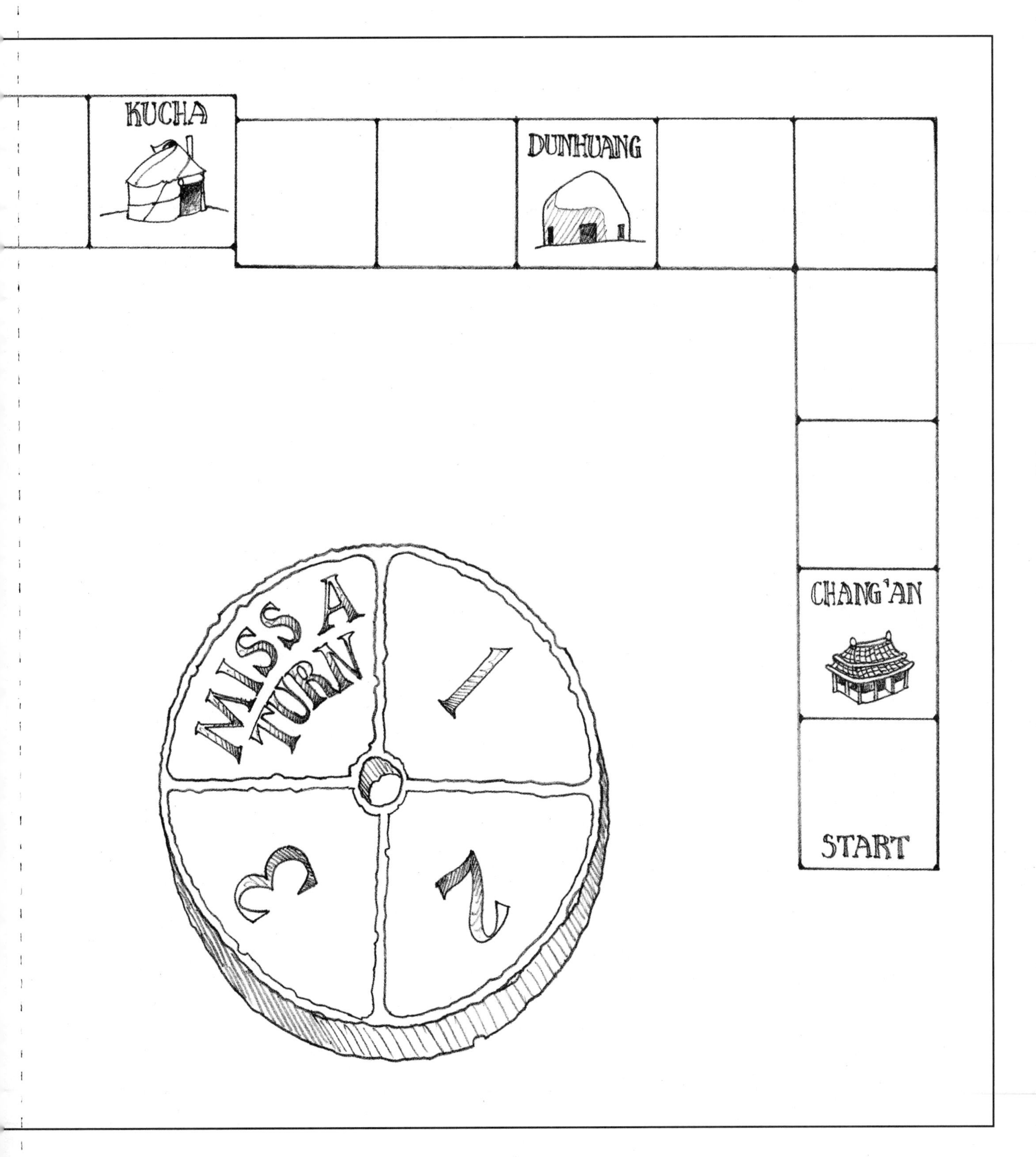

TIMELINE CHALLENGE 4

Use the timeline below to help you complete Items A–F. When completed, each item should include the following:

- the date(s) and a short written description of the item.
- a simple symbol or drawing to represent the item.
- an appropriate geometric shape surrounding the symbol or drawing. The shapes correspond to the categories listed above the right side of the timeline.
- a color bar or dot in the appropriate location on the timeline.
- a line connecting the bar or dot to the geometric shape.

A. 1700 – 1200 B.C.E.
Bronze masterpieces are produced during the Shang dynasty.

1800 B.C.E. | 1600 B.C.E. | 1400 B.C.E. | 1200 B.C.E. | 1000 B.C.E. | 800 B.C.E.

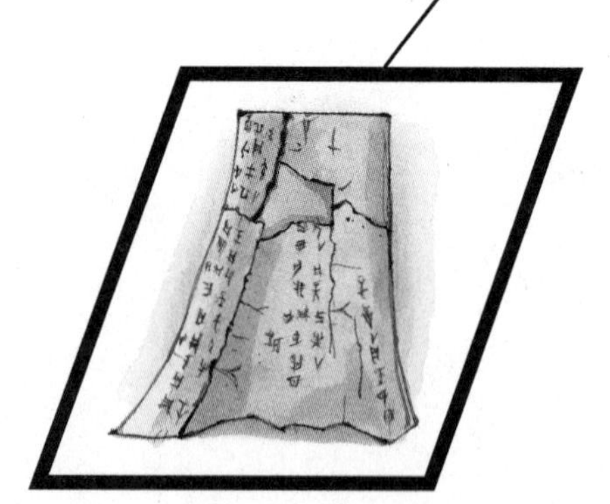

D. __________ B.C.E.
Writing appears on oracle bones.

△ Social Structure ◯ Government □ Religion ⬠ Arts ⯃ Technology ▱ Writing System

B. 1045 – 221 B.C.E.
_____________________ exists in China.

C. ______ C.E.
Buddhist writings appear in China.

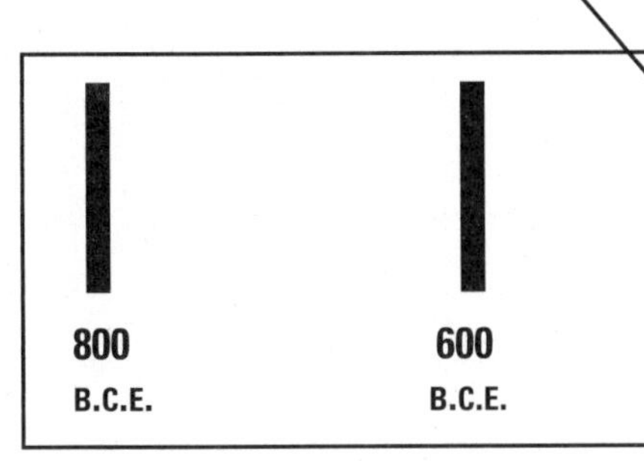

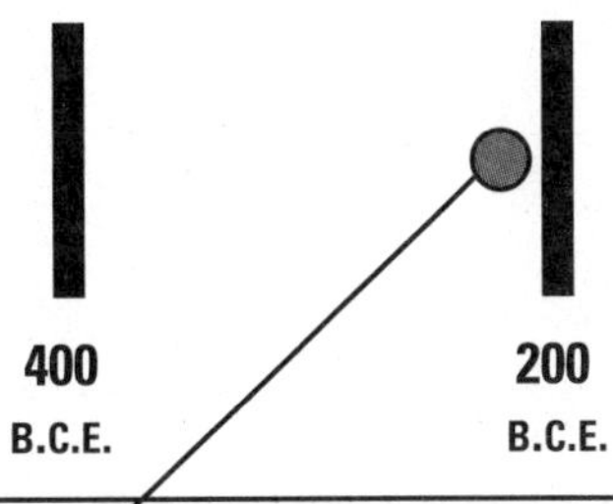

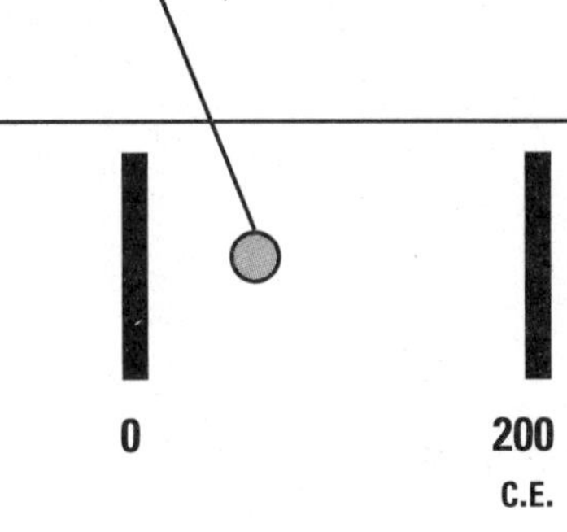

E. ______ B.C.E.
Emperor ______________________ unites China.

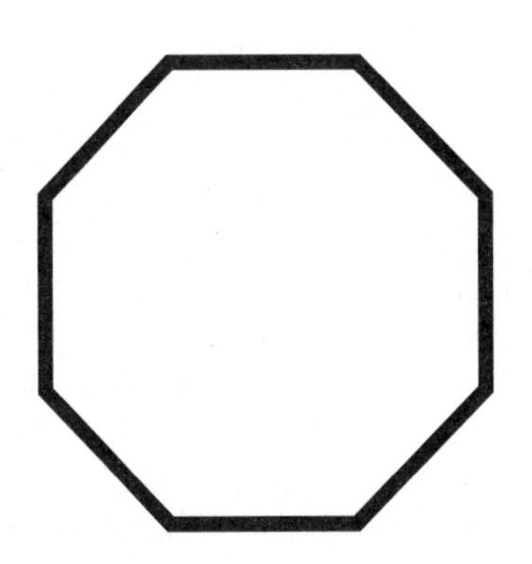

F. 105 C.E.
Emperor learns about paper.

UNIT 5

Ancient Greece

GEOGRAPHY CHALLENGE 5

To complete each Geography Challenge card, answer the questions in complete sentences. Label the map on the opposite page as directed.

Question 1 ______________________________

____

Question 2 ______________________________

____

Question 3 ______________________________

____

Question 4 ______________________________

____

Question 5 ______________________________

____

Question 6 ______________________________

____

Question 7 ______________________________

____

Question 8 ______________________________

____

GEOGRAPHY CHALLENGE 5

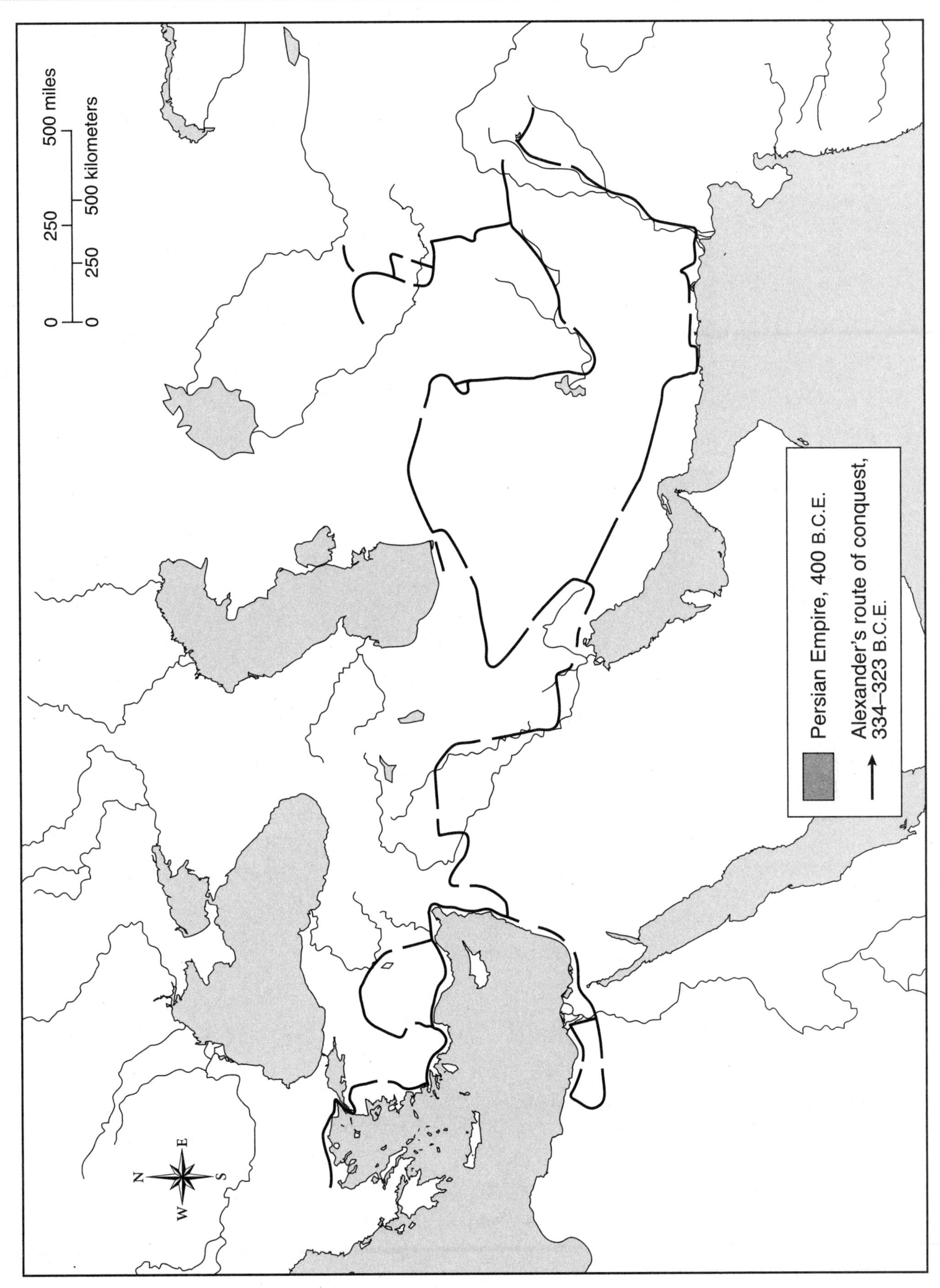

READING NOTES 25

25.1 Introduction

1. What are the mountains in Greece like?

2. Why was the sea important to the ancient Greeks?

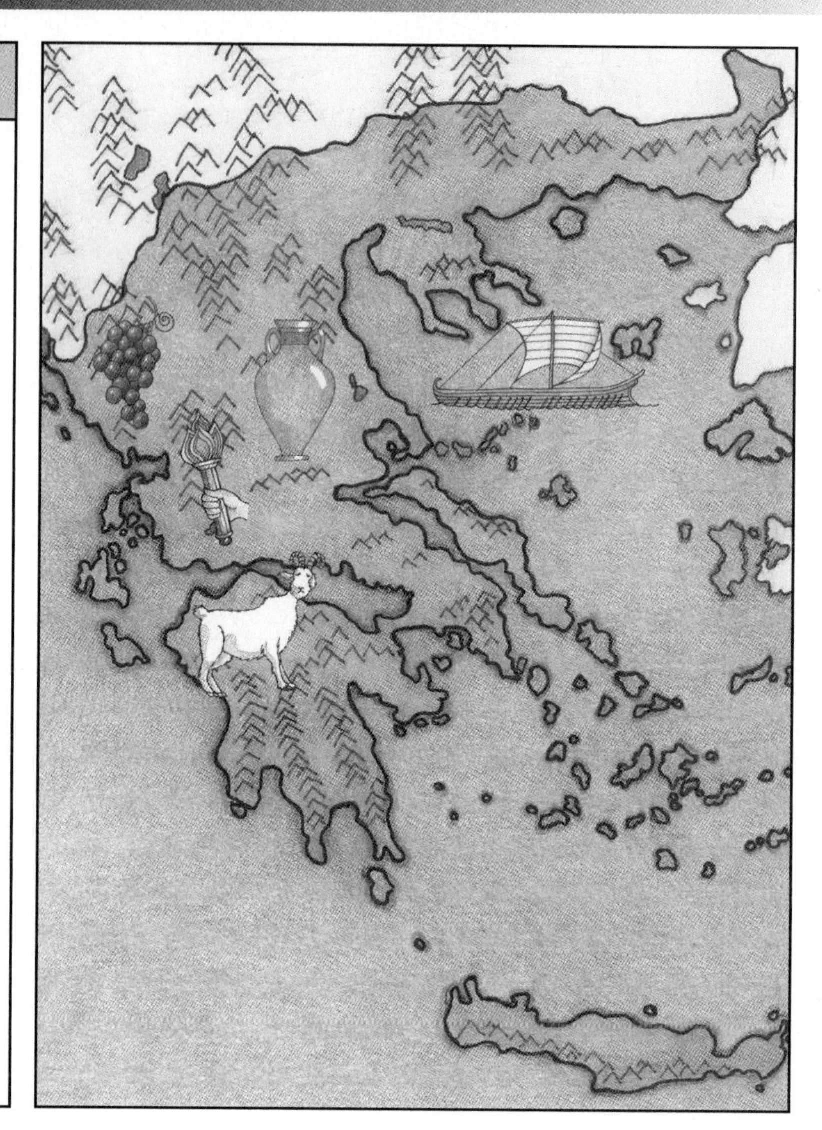

25.2 Isolated Communities and the Difficulties of Travel

1. Why were ancient Greek communities isolated from one another?

2. What were some of the dangers of travel?

3. Draw the icon from the map that represents isolation and travel.

25.3 Farming in Ancient Greece

1. List three crops Greek farmers grew and three animals they raised.

2. Why did Greek settlements often fight one another?

3. Draw the two icons from the map that represent farming.

25.4 Starting Colonies

1. Why did the Greeks start colonies?

2. Describe the steps the Greeks followed when they started a new colony.

3. Draw the icon from the map that represents starting colonies.

25.5 Trading for Needed Goods

1. Why did some Greek settlements trade?

2. What products from the Greek mainland were traded? What products did the Greeks get in exchange?

3. Draw the icon from the map that represents trading.

PROCESSING 25

Pretend that you have visited ancient Greece and have kept a scrapbook about your visit. Draw what you saw. Explain each of your pictures.

Traveling from Place to Place

____

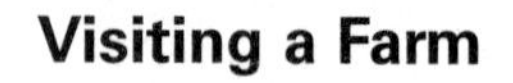

Visiting a Farm

____

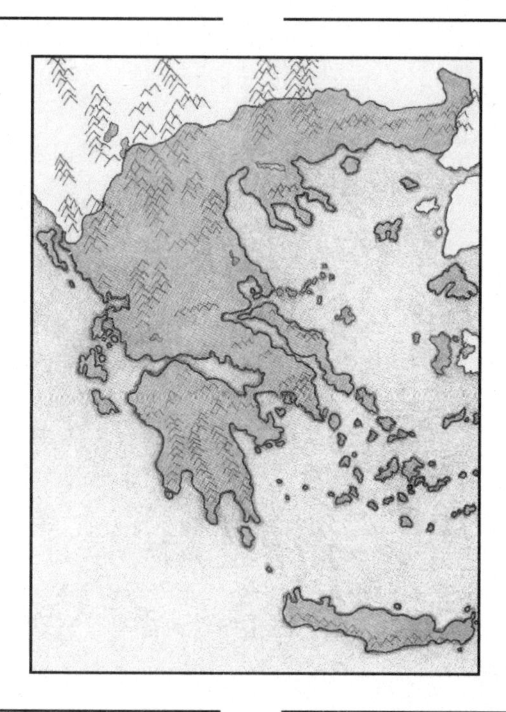

Visiting a Colony

____

Visiting a Trading Settlement

____

READING NOTES 26

Read each section in your book. Fill in the definition for each type of government, and complete the thought bubbles.

26.2 Monarchy

Under a monarchy, the power to make political decisions is in the hands of ______________________ .

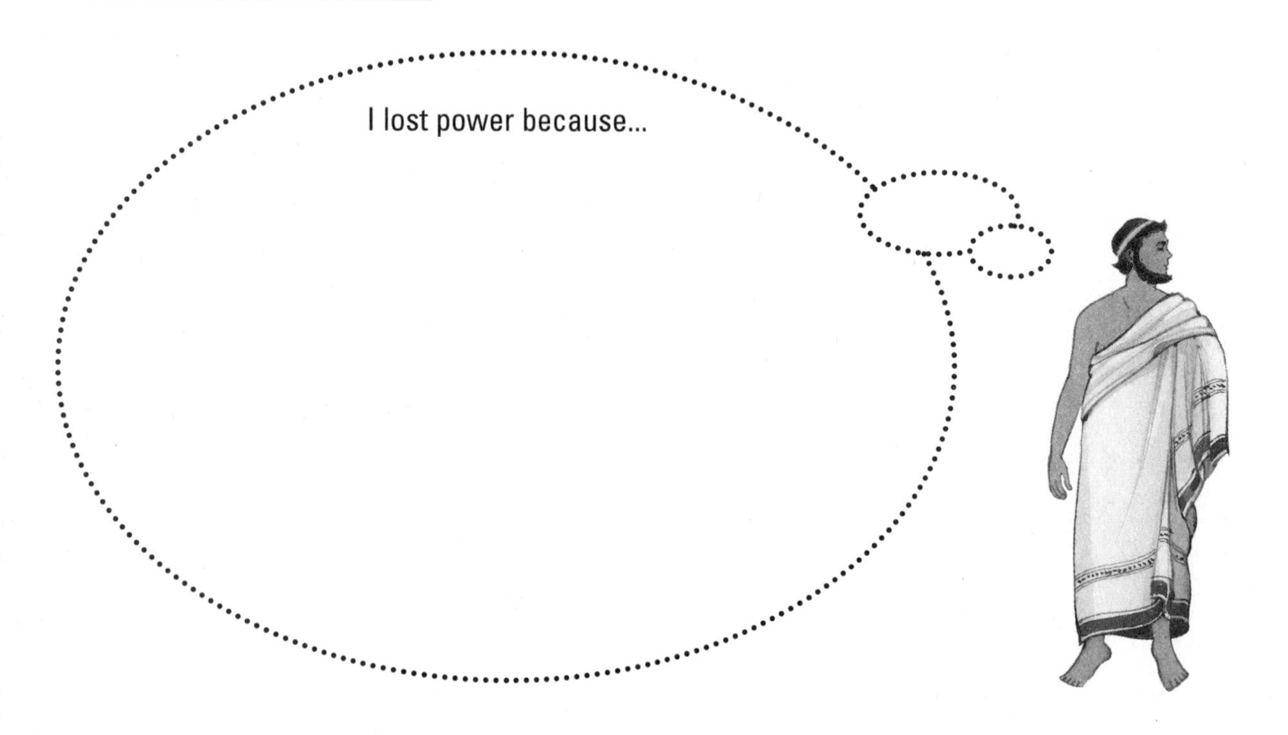

26.3 Oligarchy

Under an oligarchy, the power to make political decisions is in the hands of ______________________ .

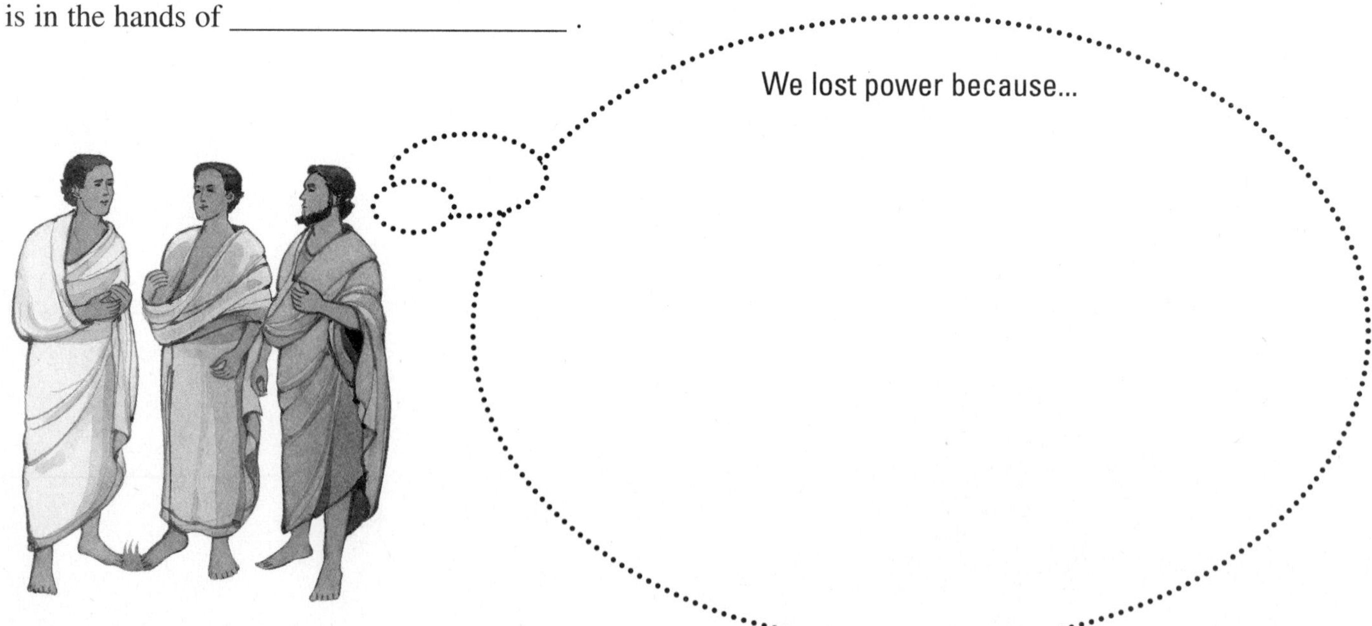

26.4 Tyranny

Under a tyranny, the power to make political decisions is in the hands of ______________________ .

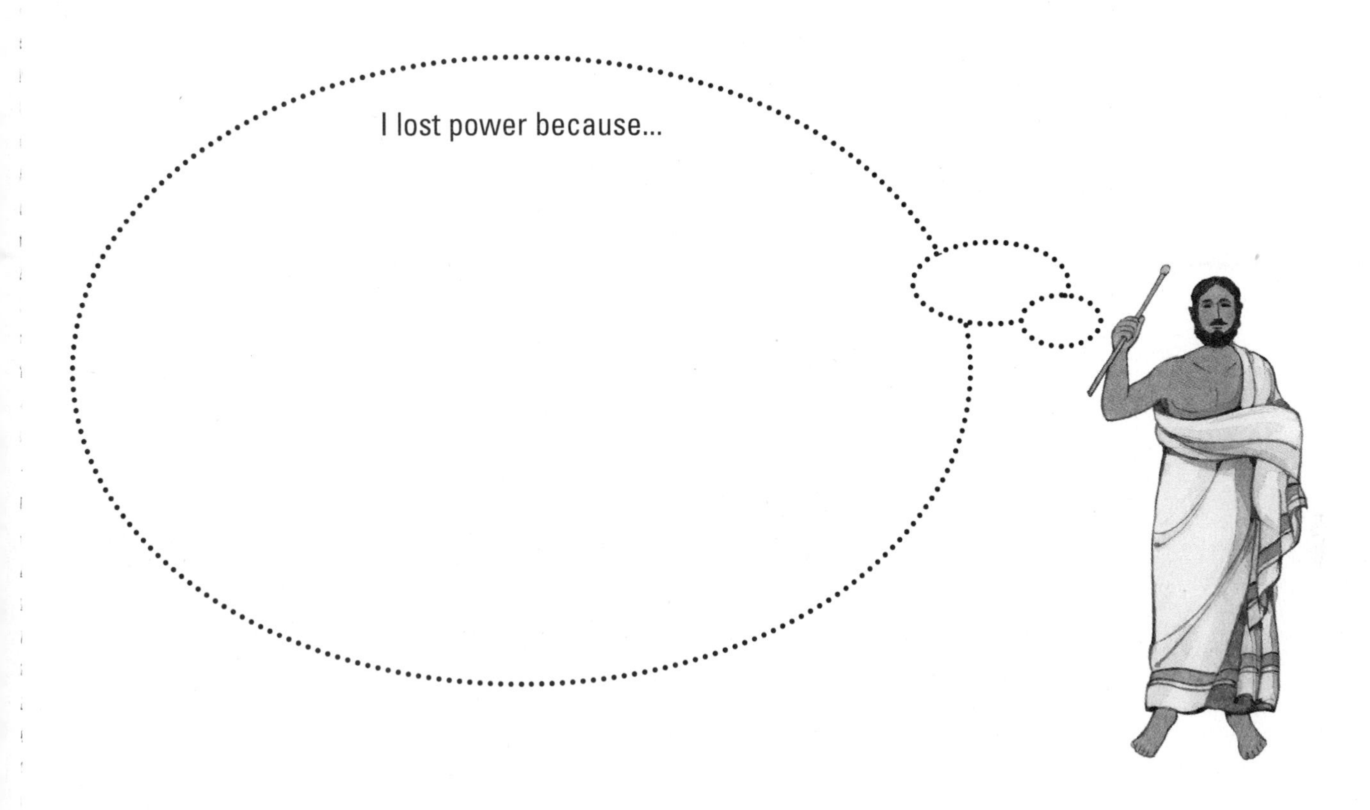

26.5 Democracy

Under a democracy, the power to make political decisions is in the hands of ______________________ .

PROCESSING 26

A *pictoword* is a drawing that uses the letters in a word to symbolize the word's meaning. Below are two pictowords for the word *vote*.

Create a pictoword for each form of government that was practiced in ancient Greece: *monarchy, oligarchy, tyranny,* and *democracy*.

PREVIEW 27

Read the descriptions below of two types of classrooms. Decide which type you prefer. At the bottom of the page, write three or four sentences that explain why you would want to be in this type of class.

Ms. Foster's class: Ms. Foster believes that students should help to make the classroom rules. The class votes on such rules as whether they can chew gum in class, eat in class, leave their seats whenever they want, speak without raising their hands, and wear hats in class. Students also vote on the punishments for breaking any rules.

Ms. Kobe's class: Ms. Kobe sets the rules for the class. The rules are quite strict. Students may not chew gum or eat in class. They cannot leave their seats unless they raise their hands and ask permission. No hats are allowed. Students may not talk when Ms. Kobe is giving a lesson. Ms. Kobe also has strict punishments. If a student breaks any rule, she or he must spend one hour after school cleaning the classroom.

I would want to be in Ms. ___________________'s class because...

READING NOTES 27

Make a sketch of each metope you see on the Athenian temple. Then answer the question in the corresponding box. Give at least three answers to each question.

27.3 Athenian Government	27.4 Athenian Economy
Why was Athens called a democracy?	How did Athenians get the goods they needed for everyday life?

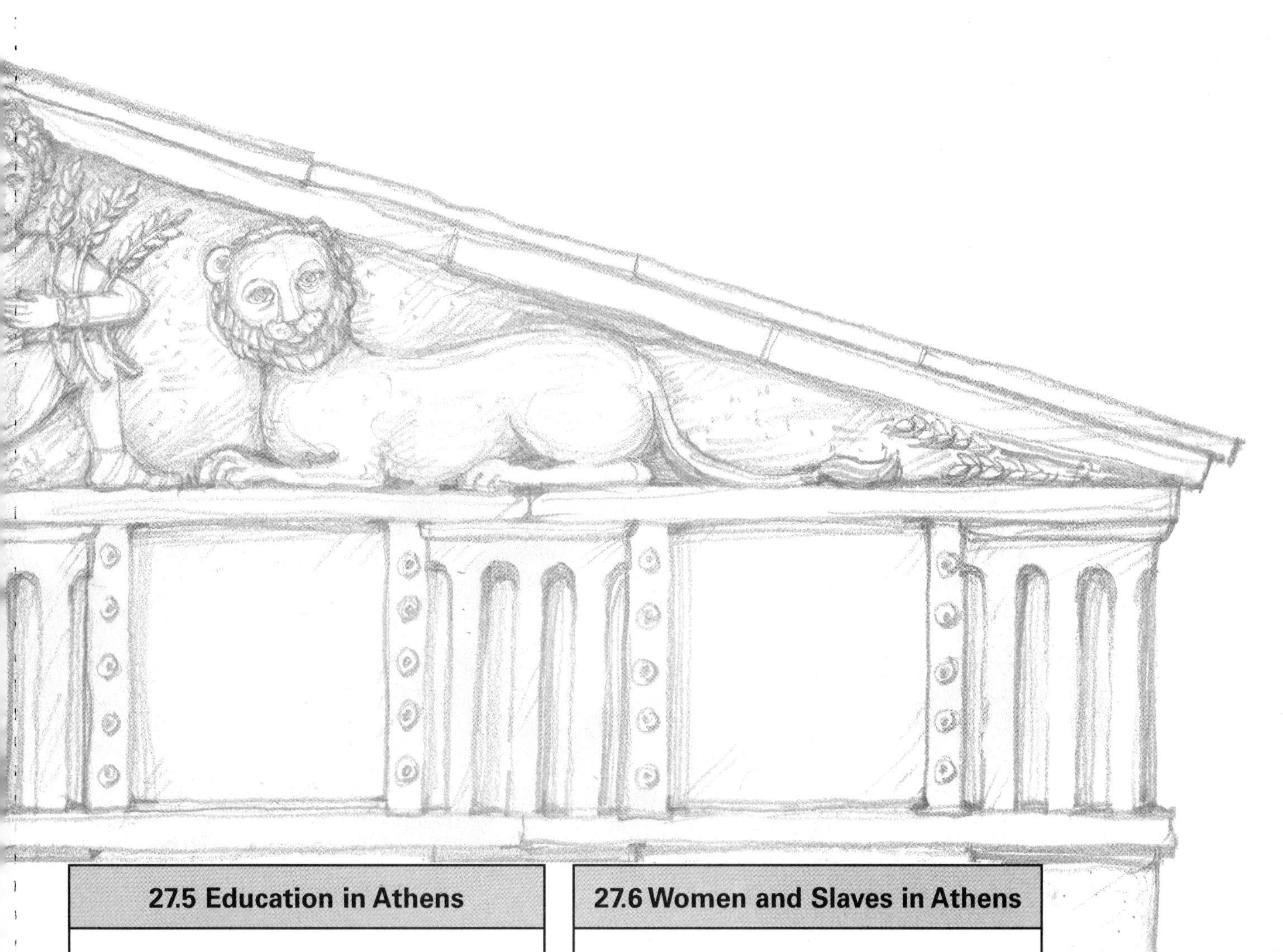

27.5 Education in Athens	27.6 Women and Slaves in Athens
How did Athenians train the minds and bodies of boys?	How were women and slaves treated in Athens?

READING NOTES 27

Make a sketch of each metope you see on the Spartan temple. Then answer the question in the corresponding box. Give at least three answers to each question.

27.7 Spartan Government	27.8 Spartan Economy
Why was Sparta called an oligarchy?	How did Spartans get the goods they needed for everyday life?

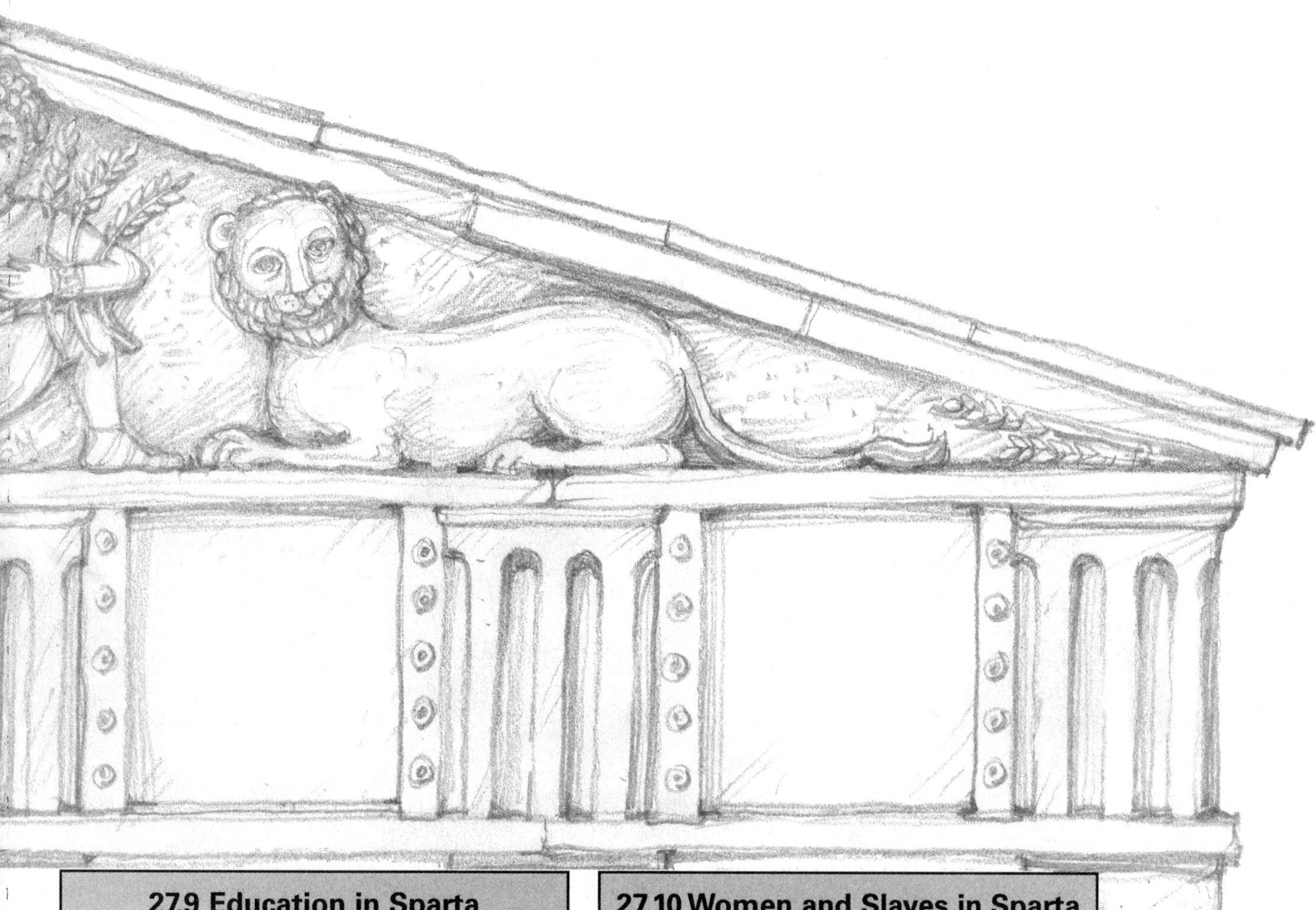

27.9 Education in Sparta	27.10 Women and Slaves in Sparta
How did Spartans train boys and girls so they could protect the city-state?	How were women and slaves treated in Sparta?

PROCESSING 27

In the area where the plates below overlap, list things that are the same about Athens and Sparta. List things that are different about Athens and Sparta in the parts of the plates that do not overlap. Add two pictures to each plate to illustrate aspects of life in Athens and Sparta.

Follow along with the paragraph below as your teacher plays the CD, and then complete the chart.

Hello, sports fans!

Here we are at Miles Pavilion to watch the Wildcats take on the Lions in this championship basketball game. To be honest with you folks, I don't see how the Wildcats have a chance, and I'm afraid this game is going to be a real blowout. The Lions have a tremendously strong coach—and don't forget that great Lions' captain who is so respected by the team. Check out those great uniforms—the Lions' sponsors certainly shower the team with everything they need. The Wildcats are really outmatched. They don't even have a coach! It's really sad to see the way the team members are constantly fighting with each other. Just look, folks, at the shabby way the team is dressed. Why, I even see one member who doesn't have shoes! This team certainly doesn't have any money. Well, who do *you* think will win this game?

Team Evaluation Chart		
	Lions	Wildcats
Strengths		
Weaknesses		

READING NOTES 28

Step 1: Identify eight details in this image of Darius at a war council. Draw a line to each detail, and label it.

Step 2: Write three guesses about what is happening at this council of war. Support each guess with details from the picture.

1. ______________________________

2. ______________________________

3. ______________________________

Step 3: Read Section 28.2. Answer the questions below.

1. Why did the Ionians revolt against Persian rule?

2. What happened to the Ionians?

Step 4: Circle the soldier who represents the stronger force at this time.

Persian soldier

Greek soldier

Step 1: Identify eight details in this image of the Battle of Marathon. Draw a line to each detail, and label it.

Step 2: Write three guesses, based on what you see, about what is happening at the Battle of Marathon.

1. ________________________________

2. ________________________________

3. ________________________________

Step 3: Read Section 28.3. Answer the questions below.

1. What happened at Marathon?

2. Why was the Battle of Marathon important to the Greek city-states?

Step 4: Circle the soldier who represents the stronger force at this time.

Persian soldier

Greek soldier

READING NOTES 28

Step 1: Identify eight details in this image of the Battle of Thermopylae. Draw a line to each detail, and label it.

Step 2: Write three guesses, based on what you see, about what is happening at Battle of Thermopylae.

1. ____

2. ____

3. ____

Step 3: Read Section 28.4. Answer the questions below.

1. How were the Spartans able to hold off such a large Persian army?

2. How were the Persians eventually able to defeat the Spartans?

3. Why did the Spartans refuse to escape although they knew they would be killed?

Step 4: Circle the soldier who represents the stronger force at this time.

Persian soldier

Greek soldier

Step 1: Identify eight details in this image of the Battle of Salamis. Draw a line to each detail, and label it.

Step 2: Write three guesses, based on what you see, about what is happening at the Battle of Salamis.

1. ______________________________

2. ______________________________

3. ______________________________

Step 3: Read Section 28.5. Answer the questions below.

1. Why did the Athenians sail to nearby islands in panic?

2. How were the Greeks able to defeat the Persian fleet, even though they were outnumbered?

Step 4: Circle the soldier who represents the stronger force at this time.

Persian soldier

Greek soldier

READING NOTES 28

Step 1: Identify eight details in this image of the Battle of Plataea. Draw a line to each detail, and label it.

Step 2: Write three guesses, based on what you see, about what is happening at the Battle of Plataea.

1. ____

2. ____

3. ____

Step 3: Read Sections 28.6 and 28.7. Answer the questions below.

1. What happened at the Battle of Plataea?

2. Why were the Persian wars important?

Step 4: Circle the soldier who represents the stronger force at this time.

Persian soldier

Greek soldier

Use your knowledge of the Persian Wars to write a headline for each picture.

PREVIEW 29

Write a short paragraph in answer to the question below.

Historians often refer to the period between 479 and 431 B.C.E. in Athenian history as Athens' Golden Age. What does this suggest to you about life in Athens during this time?

READING NOTES 29

For each section of the Reading Notes, use a different color marker to outline the box and show where you are on the map. Then answer the questions in each box.

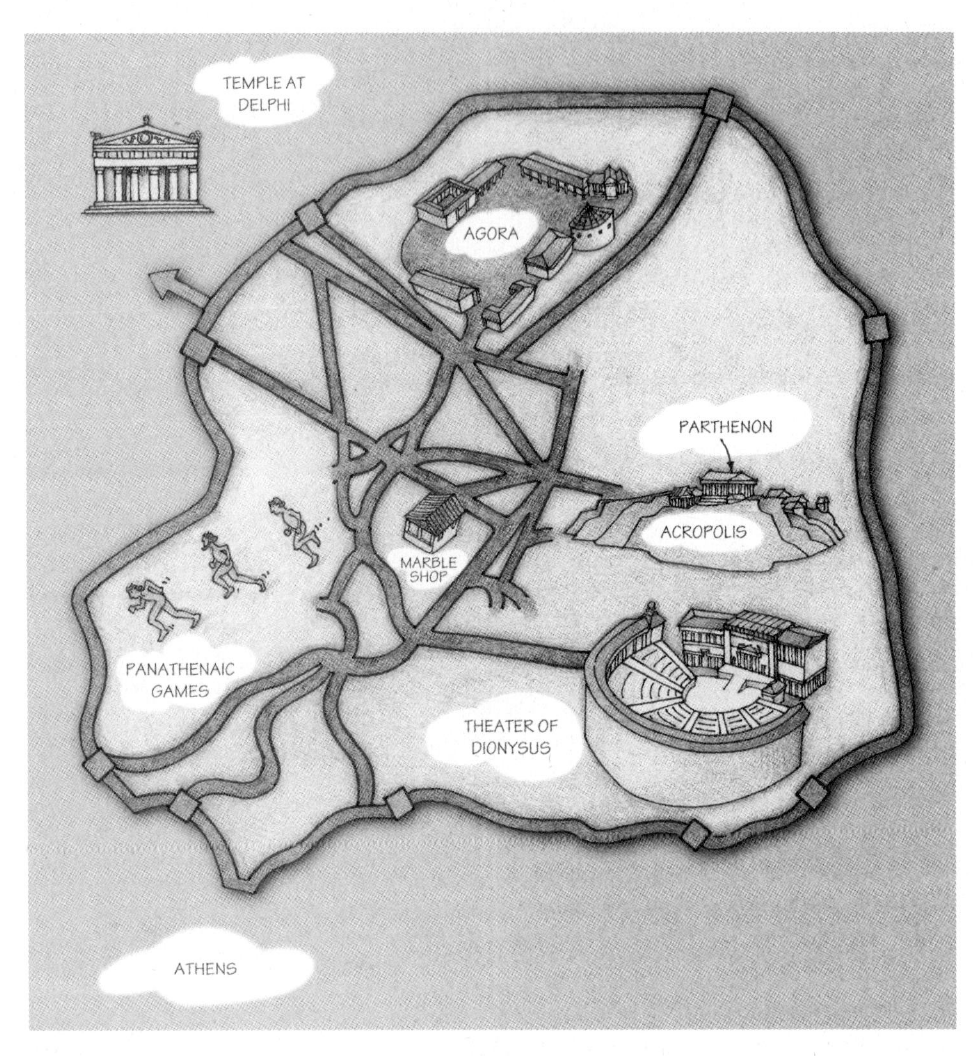

29.2 A City of Contrasts

Why can Athens be called a city of contrasts?

29.3 Religion: The Temple at Delphi

1. In what ways did Greek gods and goddesses play an important part in the lives of the Athenians?
2. What were the Greek gods and goddesses like?
3. Why did the Greeks go to Delphi?

29.4 Architecture: The Acropolis

1. What was the Parthenon?

2. On this sketch of the Parthenon, label these parts: *pediment, frieze, Doric column.*

29.5 Sculpture: A Marble Workshop

1. How did Athenian sculpture change over the years?

2. Who was Phidias? What did he do?

29.6 Drama: The Theater of Dionysus

List three ways Greek drama differed from plays and movies of today.

29.7 Philosophy: The Agora

1. What do philosophers do?

2. How did Socrates try to teach others?

3. What happened to Socrates?

29.8 Sports: The Panathenaic Games

1. What was the purpose of athletic events in Greece?

2. Describe one Panathenaic event that is part of our present Olympics.

3. Describe one Panathenaic event that is not part of our present Olympics.

PREVIEW 30

Draw a figure to represent a good leader. Around the figure, list five characteristics that you believe make a good leader. Draw a line from each characteristic to the part of the figure that symbolizes that characteristic. For example, if a good leader should be persuasive, write the word *Persuasive* beside the figure. Then draw a line from the word to the figure's mouth.

Read Critical Thinking Question A, and then follow the steps below.

Critical Thinking Question A
Philip, the father of Alexander the Great, planned to take advantage of the wars between the Greek city-states to conquer them. How successful do you think his plan will be?

Step 1: Read Section 30.2. Explain what happened to the Greek city-states as a result of the Peloponnesian War. Write your answer below.

Step 2: Discuss these questions:

1. On a sports team, what are the disadvantages of team members fighting among themselves? What are the advantages?

2. What do you think the advantages and disadvantages were of the constant fighting among the Greek city-states?

3. If team members are constantly fighting among themselves, is it more or less likely they will be beaten by another team? Why?

4. Do you think the wars between the Greek city-states made them more or less able to resist Philip? Why?

Step 3: Rate Philip's plan to defeat the Greek city-states by taking advantage of the wars between them. Before finding out what really happened, rate the plan according to how successful you think it will be. Place your token on the spectrum below to show your rating. Be prepared to give two reasons for your rating.

Very unsuccessful | Very successful

Step 4: Share your opinions. When the teacher directs you, send your Presenter to the front of the room. The Presenter will place your Group Number sheet on the appropriate place on the spectrum on the board and explain why your group placed it there.

Step 5: Mark your spectrum. After the class discussion, decide with your group whether you wish to change your token's position. Indicate your final prediction by marking an X on the spectrum in Step 3. If necessary, change the position of your Group Number sheet on the board, and explain to the class why you made the change.

Step 6: Read Section 30.3 to find out how successful Philip's plan was.

READING NOTES 30

Read Critical Thinking Question B, and then follow the steps below.

Critical Thinking Question B
Alexander planned to use terror and kindness to conquer an empire. How successful do you think his plan will be?

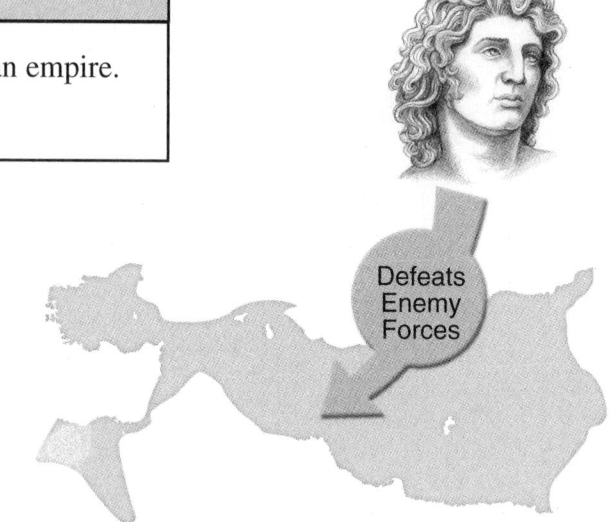

Step 1: Read Section 30.4. Write your answers to the questions below.

1. Why was Alexander well trained to be a leader?

2. Why did Alexander decide to attack Persia?

Step 2: Discuss these questions:

1. Who is more likely to get you to do something for him or her: someone who threatens to beat you up if you don't, or someone who offers you money if you do?

2. Why do you think Alexander planned to destroy some of the cities he conquered and sell the people into slavery? Do you think this was a good idea or a bad idea? Why?

3. Why do you think Alexander planned to rebuild destroyed property in some cities he conquered and appoint local leaders to rule? Do you think this was a good idea or a bad idea? Why?

Step 3: Rate Alexander's plan to use terror and kindness to conquer an empire. Before finding out what really happened, rate the plan according to how successful you think it will be. Place your token on the spectrum below to show your rating. Be prepared to give two reasons for your rating.

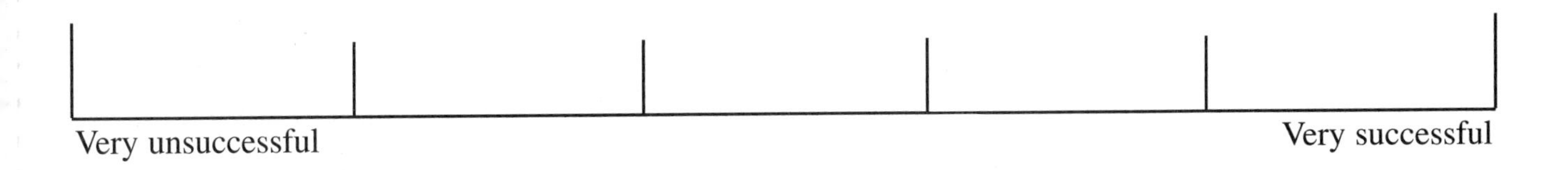

Step 4: Share your opinions. When the teacher directs you, send your Presenter to the front of the room to place your Group Number sheet on the spectrum on the board and explain why your group placed it there.

Step 5: Mark your spectrum. After the class discussion, decide with your group whether you wish to change your token's position. Indicate your final prediction by marking an X on the spectrum in Step 3. If necessary, change the position of your Group Number sheet on the board, and explain why you made the change.

Step 6: Read Section 30.5 to find out how successful the plan was.

READING NOTES 30

Read Critical Thinking Question C, and then follow the steps below.

Critical Thinking Question C
Alexander planned to unite the people he conquered by spreading Greek ideas. How successful do you think his plan will be in uniting the empire?

Step 1: Read Section 30.6. Write two ways Alexander spread Greek ideas in order to unite the different peoples of his empire.

Step 2: Discuss these questions:

1. Do you think all people living in America should learn to speak English? Why or why not?

2. Why do you think Alexander insisted that government officials and soldiers speak only Greek? Do you think that was a good idea or a bad idea? Why?

3. If you went to another country, what things from the United States might you see? When people see things from the United States in their countries, do you think it makes them respect Americans more or less? Why?

4. How do you think non-Greeks felt about Greeks when they saw Greek buildings, art, theater, literature, and government in the cities Alexander started? Do you think it made them respect the Greeks more or less? Why?

Step 3: Rate Alexander's plan to spread Greek ideas to unite his empire. Rate the plan according to how successful you think it will be. Place your token on the spectrum below to show your rating. Be prepared to give two reasons for your rating.

Very unsuccessful — Very successful

Step 4: Share your opinions. When the teacher directs you, send your Presenter to the front of the room to place your Group Number sheet on the spectrum on the board and explain why your group placed it there.

Step 5: Mark your spectrum. After the class discussion, decide with your group whether you wish to change your token's position. Indicate your final prediction by marking an X on the spectrum in Step 3. If necessary, change the position of your Group Number sheet on the board, and explain why you made the change.

Read Critical Thinking Question D, and then follow the steps below.

Critical Thinking Question D
Alexander planned to use religion to get people to accept him as their leader. He thought this would unite the people of his empire. How successful do you think his plan will be?

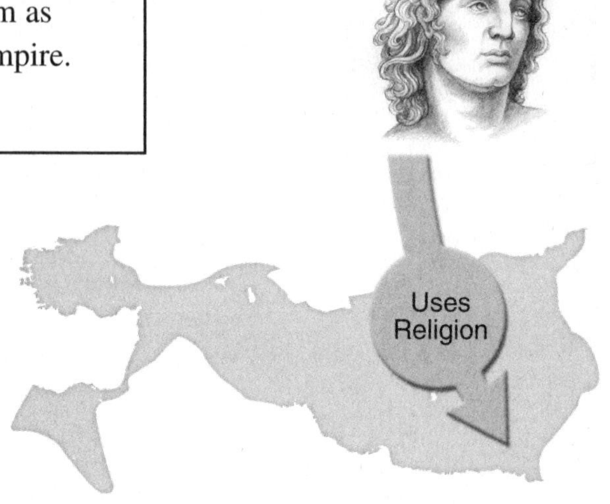

Step 1: Read Section 30.7. List two ways Alexander used religion to convince people in his empire to accept him as their leader.

Step 2: Discuss these questions:

1. Do you think it is important for your leader to follow the same religion as you do? Why or why not?

2. Why do you think Alexander treated all religions as equal? Do you think this was a good idea or a bad idea? Why?

3. If people believed that Alexander was a god, how might they feel about things he did?

4. If people did not think Alexander was a god, how might they feel about the fact that he said he was a god?

Step 3: Rate Alexander's plan to use religion to get people to accept him as their leader. Rate the plan according to how successful you think it will be. Place your token on the spectrum below to show your rating. Be prepared to give two reasons for your rating.

Very unsuccessful | | | | | Very successful

Step 4: Share your opinions. When the teacher directs you, send your Presenter to the front of the room to place your Group Number sheet on the spectrum on the board and explain why your group placed it there.

Step 5: Mark your spectrum. After the class discussion, decide with your group whether you wish to change your token's position. Indicate your final prediction by marking an X on the spectrum in Step 3. If necessary, change the position of your Group Number sheet on the board, and explain why you made the change.

READING NOTES 30

Read Critical Thinking Question E, and then follow the steps below.

Critical Thinking Question E
Alexander planned to unite the people he conquered by adopting some of their cultural practices. How successful do you think his plan will be in uniting his empire?

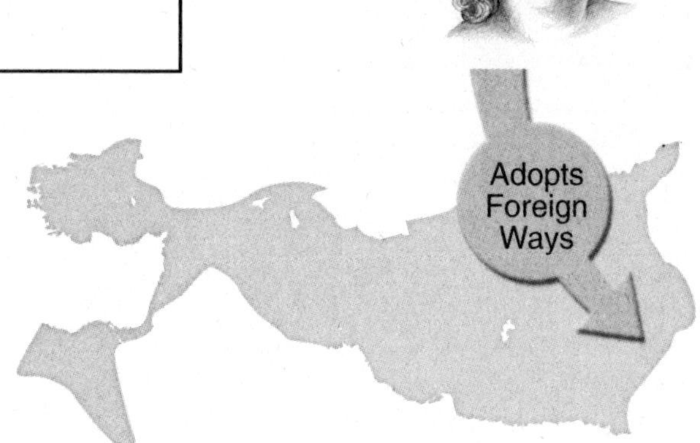

Step 1: Read Section 30.8. Write four foreign ideas or customs that Alexander adopted.

Step 2: Discuss these questions:

1. When people live in another country, do you think they should dress like the people in that country, or wear the same clothes they usually wear? Why?

2. Why do you think Alexander wore Persian clothes? Do you think this was a good idea or a bad idea?

3. Suppose a child has a mother from one country and a father from another country. How might that affect the languages the child speaks, the foods he or she eats, and the holidays he or she celebrates?

4. Why do you think Alexander encouraged marriages between Macedonians and Persians? Do you think this was a good idea or a bad idea? Why?

Step 3: Rate Alexander's plan to unite his empire by accepting foreign ways and encouraging Macedonians to do the same. Rate the plan according to how successful you think it will be. Place your token on the spectrum below to show your rating. Be prepared to give two reasons for your rating.

Very unsuccessful Very successful

Step 4: Share your opinions. When the teacher directs you, send your Presenter to the front of the room to place your Group Number sheet on the spectrum on the board and explain why your group placed it there.

Step 5: Mark your spectrum. After the class discussion, decide with your group whether you wish to change your token's position. Indicate your final prediction by marking an X on the spectrum in Step 3. If necessary, change the position of your Group Number sheet on the board, and explain why you made the change.

PROCESSING 30

Design four medallions that commemorate different parts of Alexander's plans to conquer and unite his empire. Color your illustrations. Then write a brief explanation of what each medallion shows.

PREVIEW 31

Think about an event you would like to start, an invention you would like to create, or a discovery you would like to make that would be used by future generations. For example, you might like to start a new sport, invent a gas to neutralize air pollution, or discover a cure for a disease. Draw and label your idea below. Then explain why future generations might use your contribution.

READING NOTES 31

Match the aspect of modern-day life described on each "Greek Contribution" strip with a placard showing the ancient Greek contribution that made it possible. Once you have located the placard, check your answer with your teacher. Then read the corresponding section in *History Alive! The Ancient World* and complete the Reading Notes for that section.

31.2 Greek Contributions to Modern Language and Literature

Placard ___ shows a Greek contribution to English language and literature.

1. In the gift box below, draw and label a picture to illustrate an ancient Greek contribution to English language and literature.

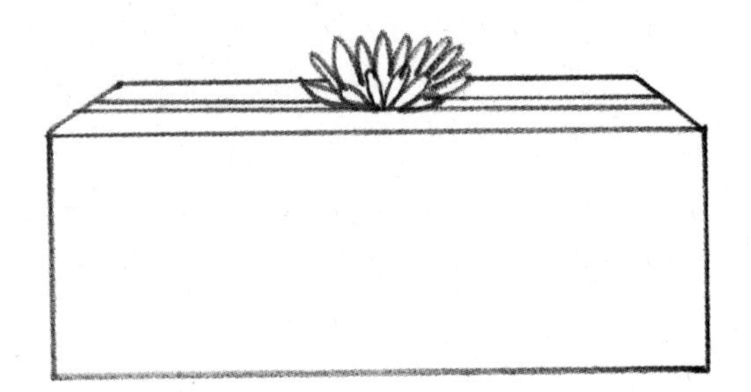

2. List another contribution the ancient Greeks made to English language and literature.

____

3. Punctuation, which came from the Greeks, can change the meaning of a sentence. Read the sentences below. Circle the sentence that means "Cats Rule!"

   My cat knows its master.

   My cat knows it's master.

31.3 Greek Contributions to Modern Government

Placard ___ shows a Greek contribution to our form of government.

1. In the gift box below, draw and label a picture to illustrate an ancient Greek contribution to our government.

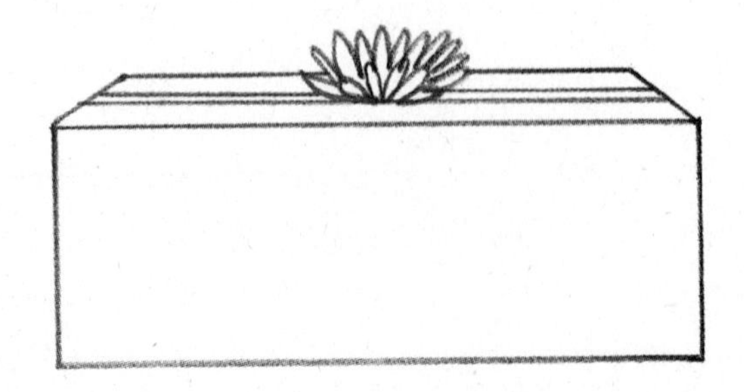

2. List another contribution the ancient Greeks made to our government.

____

3. Is the best person always elected in a democracy? Why or why not?

____

31.4 Greek Contributions to Modern Medicine

Placard ___ shows a Greek contribution to modern medical practices.

1. In the gift box below, draw and label a picture to illustrate an ancient Greek contribution to modern medicine.

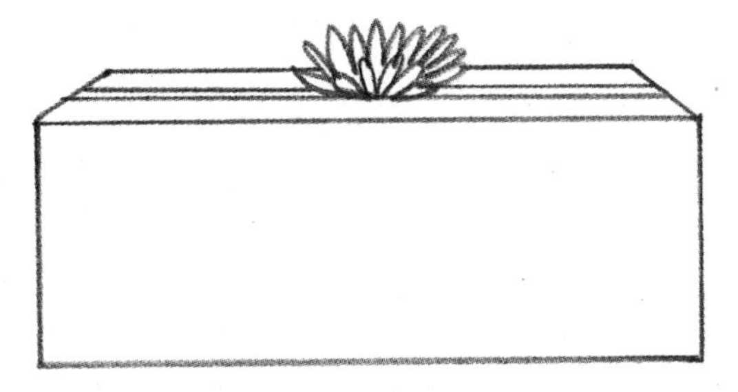

2. List another contribution the ancient Greeks made to modern medicine.

____

3. As in ancient Greece, there are still many unscientific beliefs about diseases and cures. For instance, some people believe you can get a wart by touching a frog. Below, describe another unscientific belief about some disease.

____

31.5 Greek Contributions to the Modern Understanding of the Body

Placard ___ shows a Greek contribution to our understanding of the human body.

1. In the gift box below, draw and label a picture to illustrate an ancient Greek contribution to the modern understanding of the body.

2. List another contribution the ancient Greeks made to our understanding of the body.

____

3. When we cut ourselves, why do we bleed?

____

31.6 Greek Contributions to Modern Mathematics

Placard ___ shows a Greek contribution to modern mathematics.

1. In the gift box below, draw and label a picture to illustrate an ancient Greek contribution to modern mathematics.

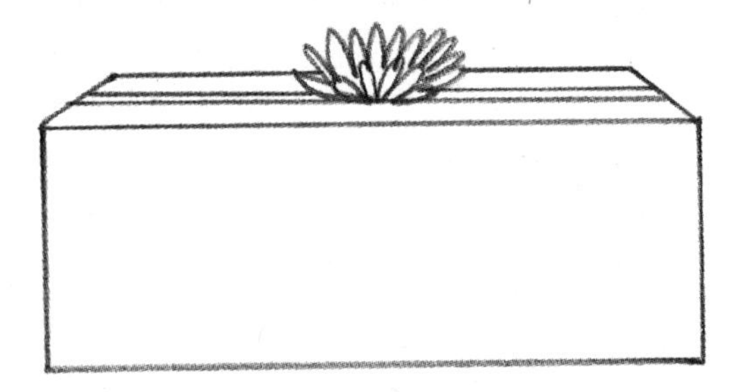

2. List another contribution of the ancient Greeks to modern mathematics.

____

3. Suppose you want to cover the floor of a closet with tile. The floor measures 3 feet by 3 feet. Each tile is 1 foot by 1 foot. How many tiles will you need? Draw a diagram of the completed floor below. Write an equation for finding its area.

31.7 Greek Contributions to Modern Astronomy

Placard ___ shows a Greek contribution to modern astronomy.

1. In the gift box below, draw and label a picture to illustrate an ancient Greek contribution to modern astronomy.

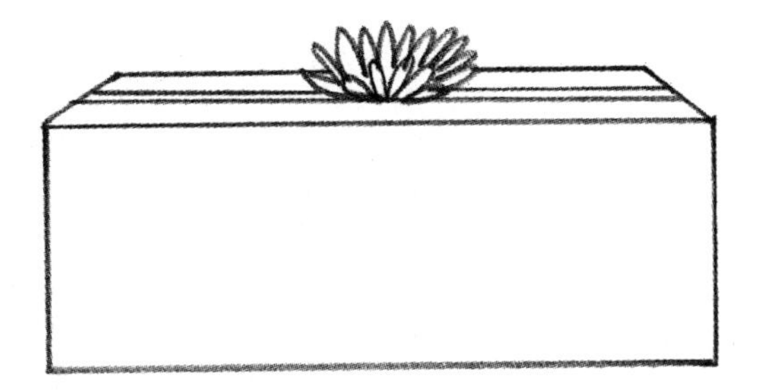

2. List another contribution of the ancient Greeks to modern astronomy.

____

3. List one reason it is important to know that Earth is round.

____

31.8 Greek Contributions to Modern Geography

Placard ___ shows a Greek contribution to our understanding of geography.

1. In the gift box below, draw and label a picture to illustrate an ancient Greek contribution to modern geography.

2. List another contribution of the ancient Greeks to modern geography.

____

3. If you were on a sinking boat, how could you let rescuers know your location?

____

31.9 Greek Contributions to the Modern Understanding of Plants and Animals

Placard ___ shows a Greek contribution to our understanding of plants and animals.

1. In the gift box below, draw and label a picture to illustrate an ancient Greek contribution to our understanding of plants and animals.

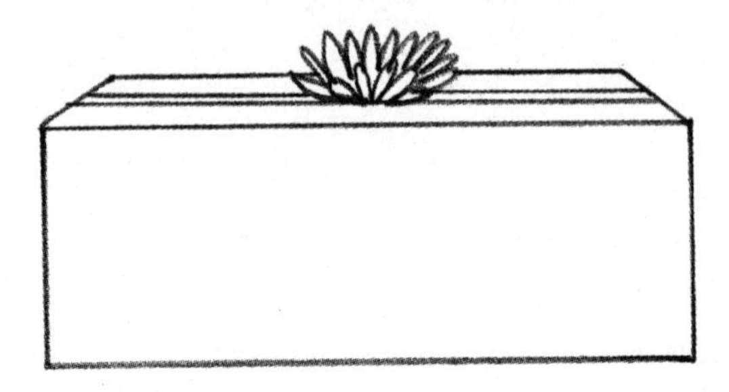

2. List another contribution of the ancient Greeks to our understanding of plants and animals.

____

3. Why is it important to be able to tell one kind of plant from another?

____

31.10 Greek Contributions to Modern Architecture

Placard ___ shows a Greek contribution to building design.

1. In the gift box below, draw and label a picture to illustrate an ancient Greek contribution to architecture.

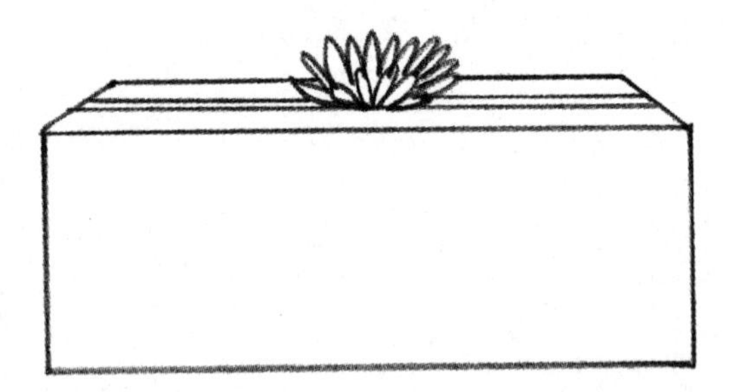

2. List another contribution of the ancient Greeks to modern architecture.

____

3. Why do you think elements of Greek architecture are often seen on banks, schools, government buildings, libraries, and museums?

____

31.11 Greek Contributions to the Modern Theater

Placard ___ shows a Greek contribution to the modern theater.

1. In the gift box below, draw and label a picture to illustrate an ancient Greek contribution to the modern theater.

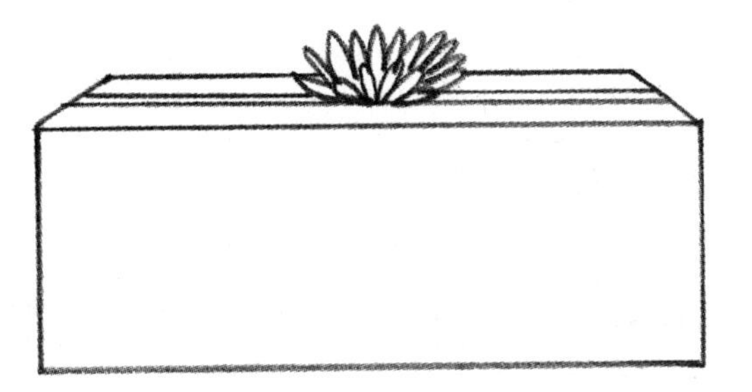

2. List another contribution of the ancient Greeks to the modern theater.

___

3. Describe the best stunt or special effect that you have seen in a play or movie.

___

31.12 Greek Contributions to Modern Sports

Placard ___ shows a Greek contribution to modern sports.

1. In the gift box below, draw and label a picture to illustrate an ancient Greek contribution to modern sports.

2. List another contribution of the ancient Greeks to modern sports.

___

3. In ancient Greece, only Greek citizens could participate in the Olympics. Today, athletes from all over the world compete. What difference do you think this makes to the Games?

___

PROCESSING 31

Pretend that the U.S. Postal Service has decided to issue a series of stamps celebrating the contributions of the ancient Greeks to our modern world. Create stamps to show as many contributions as you like. The stamps should have pictures to represent each contribution and a word that describes the contribution. Below the stamps, write a brief explanation of the importance of the contributions you have included.

About My Stamps

TIMELINE CHALLENGE 5

Use the timeline below to help you complete Items A–F. When completed, each item should include the following:

- the date(s) and a short written description of the item.
- a simple symbol or visual to represent the item.
- an appropriate geometric shape surrounding the symbol or drawing. The shapes correspond to the categories in the box above the right side of the timeline.
- a color bar or dot in the appropriate location on the timeline.
- a line connecting the bar or dot to the geometric shape.

A. 776 B.C.E.
First ____________________
are held, in honor of Zeus.

B. 507 B.C.E.
Athenian constitution gives political rights to men. Women and slaves are denied political rights.

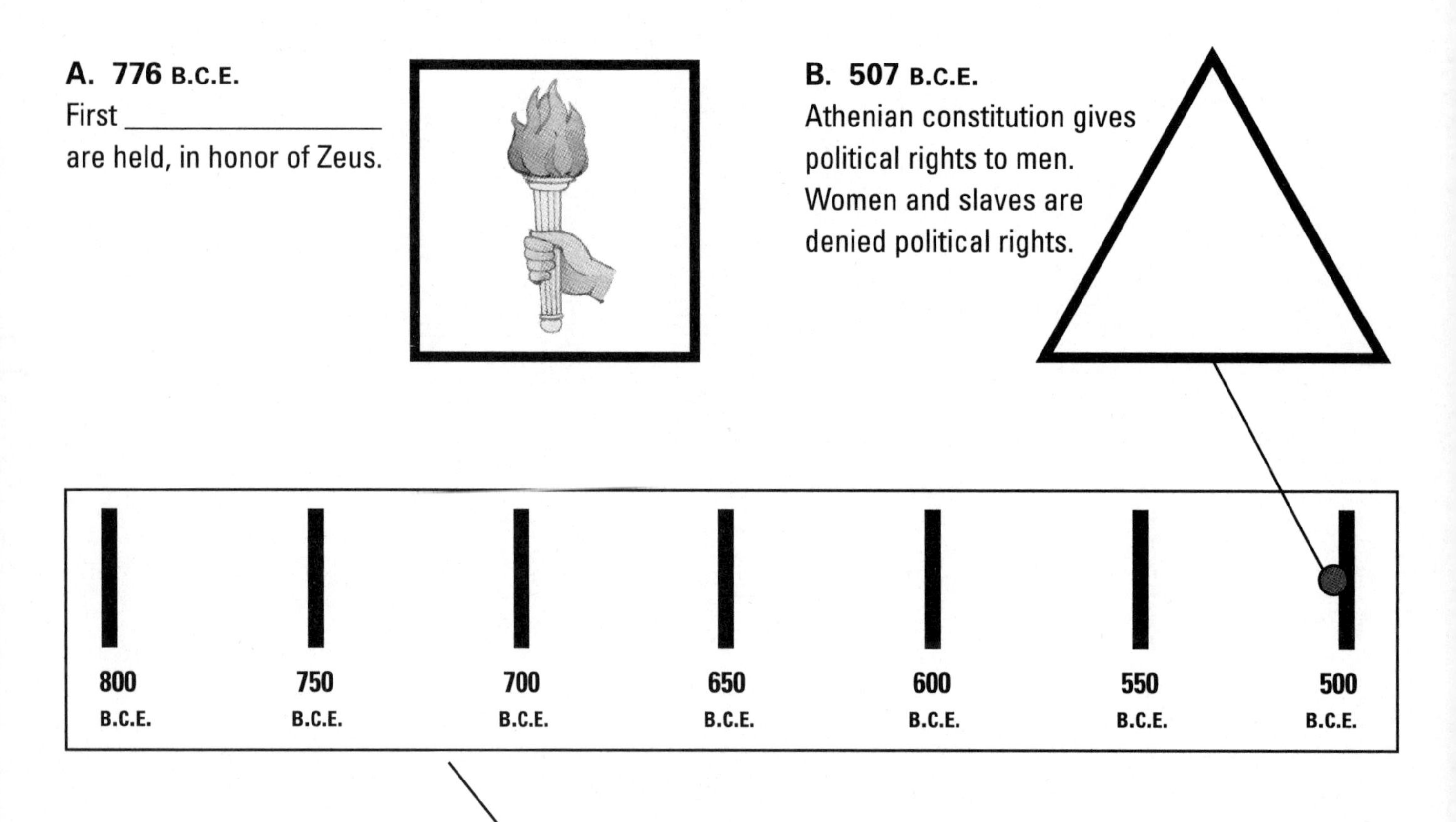

αβχδ

D. 800 – 700 B.C.E.
Greeks adopt Phoenician writing.

TIMELINE CHALLENGE 5

△ Social Structure ○ Government □ Religion ⬠ Arts ⯃ Technology ▱ Writing System

C. 499 – 479 B.C.E.
Persian wars are fought.

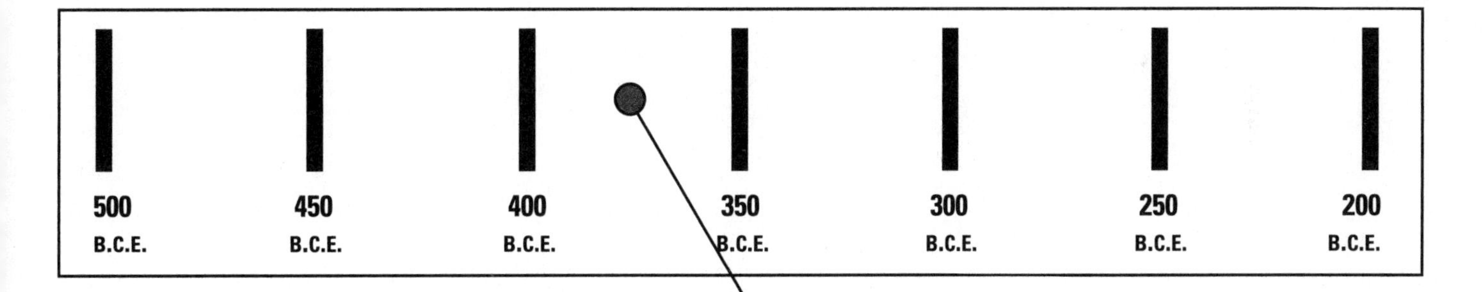

E. 447 – 438 B.C.E.
Parthenon is built.

F. _______ B.C.E.
Hippocrates, the father of ____________, dies.

UNIT 6

Ancient Rome

GEOGRAPHY CHALLENGE 6

To complete each Geography Challenge card, answer the questions in complete sentences. Label the map on the opposite page as directed.

Question 1 ______________________________

____

Question 2 ______________________________

____

Question 3 ______________________________

____

Question 4 ______________________________

____

Question 5 ______________________________

____

Question 6 ______________________________

____

Question 7 ______________________________

____

Question 8 ______________________________

____

N
E
S
W
BRITIAN

PREVIEW 32

Examine the two images of ancient Greek and Roman life. Then do the following:

- Draw three simple pictures of features that are found in both images.
- Label each feature.
- Beneath your drawings, explain why you think these features are found in both ancient Greece and ancient Rome.

For each of Sections 32.3–32.8, first read that section of *History Alive! The Ancient World*. For each section, mark the image as directed by your teacher. Then answer the question.

32.3 Etruscan Engineering

How did Etruscan engineering influence Roman life?

32.4 Etruscan Sporting Events

How did Etruscan sporting events influence Roman life?

32.5 Greek Architecture

How did Greek architecture influence Roman life?

32.6 Greek Writing

How did Greek writing influence Roman life?

32.7 Greek Art

How did Greek art influence Roman life?

32.8 Greek Mythology

How did Greek mythology influence Roman life?

PROCESSING 32

Create two coins to commemorate Etruscan and Greek influences on Roman life. Each coin should have these features:

- a drawing representing an Etruscan or a Greek influence, such as an arch or a column
- a one- or two-sentence caption that describes the influence and explains how it affected ancient Roman life

Beneath your coins, explain why you think these Etruscan and Greek influences had the greatest impact on Roman life.

READING NOTES 33

Read Sections 33.2–33.5. For each section, make a drawing on each pan of the balance to show how power was divided in ancient Rome. The drawings representing groups with more power should be on the "weighted," or lower, pan. Then answer the questions.

33.2 Patricians and Plebeians Under Etruscan Rule

1. On the pans, draw and label stick figures to represent an Etruscan king, a patrician, and a plebeian. Give the characters facial expressions that represent how they might be feeling.

2. Who were the patricians? How much power did they have to influence the Etruscan king?

3. Who were the plebeians? How much power did they have to influence the Etruscan king?

33.3 The Patricians Create a Republic

1. On the pans, draw and label stick figures to represent a patrician and a plebeian. Give them appropriate facial expressions.

2. What was the balance of political power between patricians and plebeians when the Republic was first created?

3. Why was the balance of power between patricians and plebeians unequal?

33.4 The Plebeians Rebel

1. On the pans, draw and label stick figures to represent a patrician and a plebeian. Give them appropriate facial expressions.

2. What was the balance of political power between patricians and plebeians during the Conflict of the Orders in 494 B.C.E.?

3. Why were the patricians frightened by the actions of the plebeians?

33.5 The Plebeians Gain Political Equality

1. On the pans, draw and label stick figures to represent a patrician and a plebeian. Give them appropriate facial expressions.

2. What was the balance of political power between patricians and plebeians by 287 B.C.E.?

3. Why was there equality between patricians and plebeians by this time?

PROCESSING 33

Complete the diagram by doing the following:

1. Choose tile colors to represent plebeians and patricians. Glue them into the key.
2. For each part of government shown, glue an appropriate number of each color of tile into the spaces.
3. Beneath your drawing, explain why this form of government kept power balanced between patricians and plebeians.

Key

Patrician

Plebeian

Roman Government in 287 B.C.E.

Consuls

Senate

Tribunes

Council of Plebs

Citizen Assemblies

PREVIEW 34

Think about your school's best qualities. On the billboard, create an advertisement that your principal could use to tell members of the community about those qualities. Then add a short written statement at the bottom of the billboard to express the viewpoint of a community member with a different opinion.

READING NOTES 34

After you read each section of text, complete these steps:

1. Shade in the appropriate area of the map on the opposite page in a new color to show Roman expansion. Color in the key to match.
2. Find the corresponding column on pages 232 and 233. Trace the outline of the column with the color you used on the map.
3. Answer the questions inside the column, and fill in the missing dates.

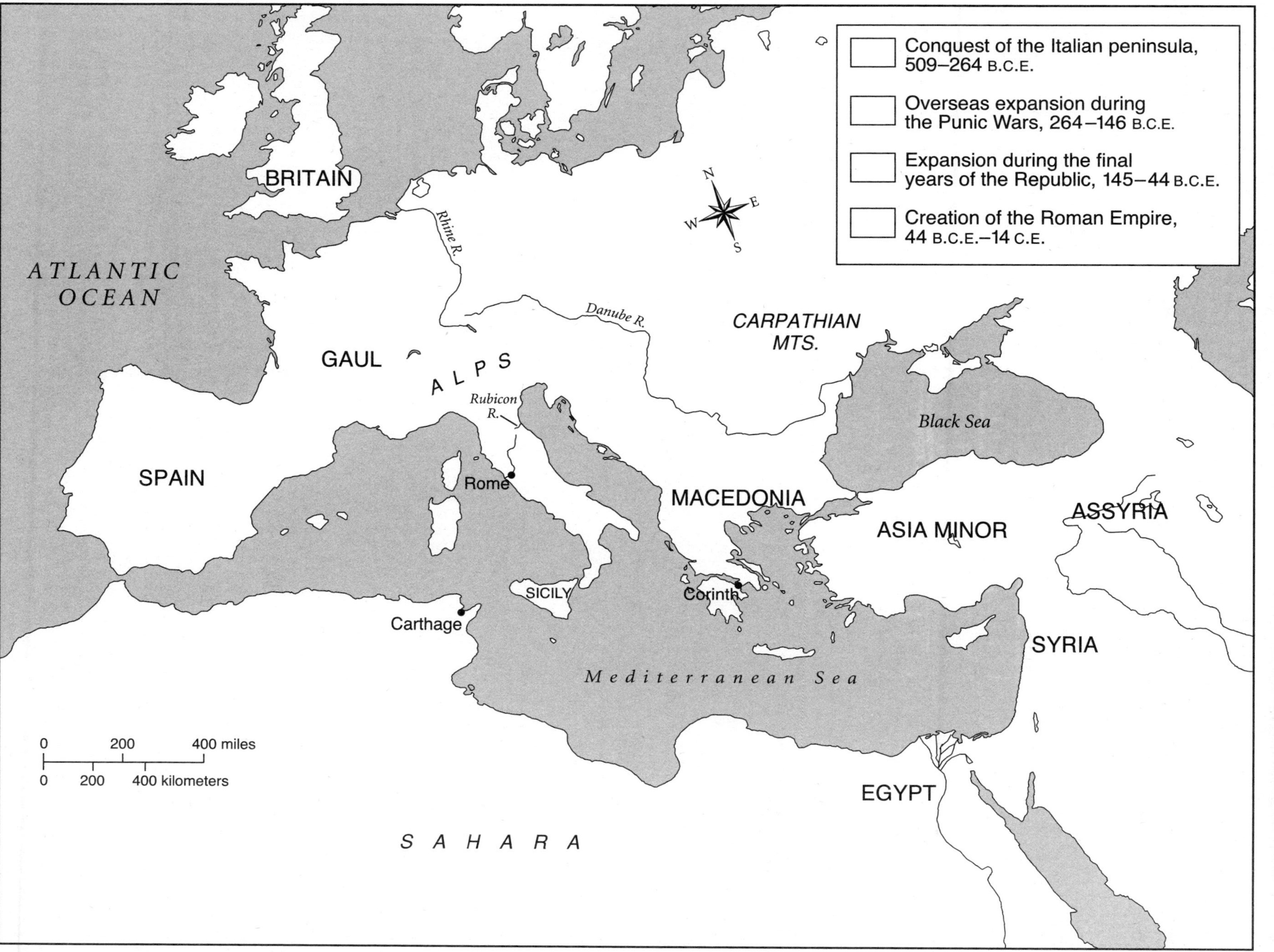

Conquest of the Italian peninsula, 509–264 B.C.E.
Overseas expansion during the Punic Wars, 264–146 B.C.E.
Expansion during the final years of the Republic, 145–44 B.C.E.
Creation of the Roman Empire, 44 B.C.E.–14 C.E.
N
E
S
W
BRITAIN
Rhine R.
ATLANTIC OCEAN
Danube R.
CARPATHIAN MTS.
GAUL
ALPS
Rubicon R.
Black Sea
SPAIN
Rome
MACEDONIA
ASSYRIA
ASIA MINOR
SICILY
Corinth
Carthage
SYRIA
Mediterranean Sea
0
200
400 miles
0
200
400 kilometers
EGYPT
SAHARA

READING NOTES 34

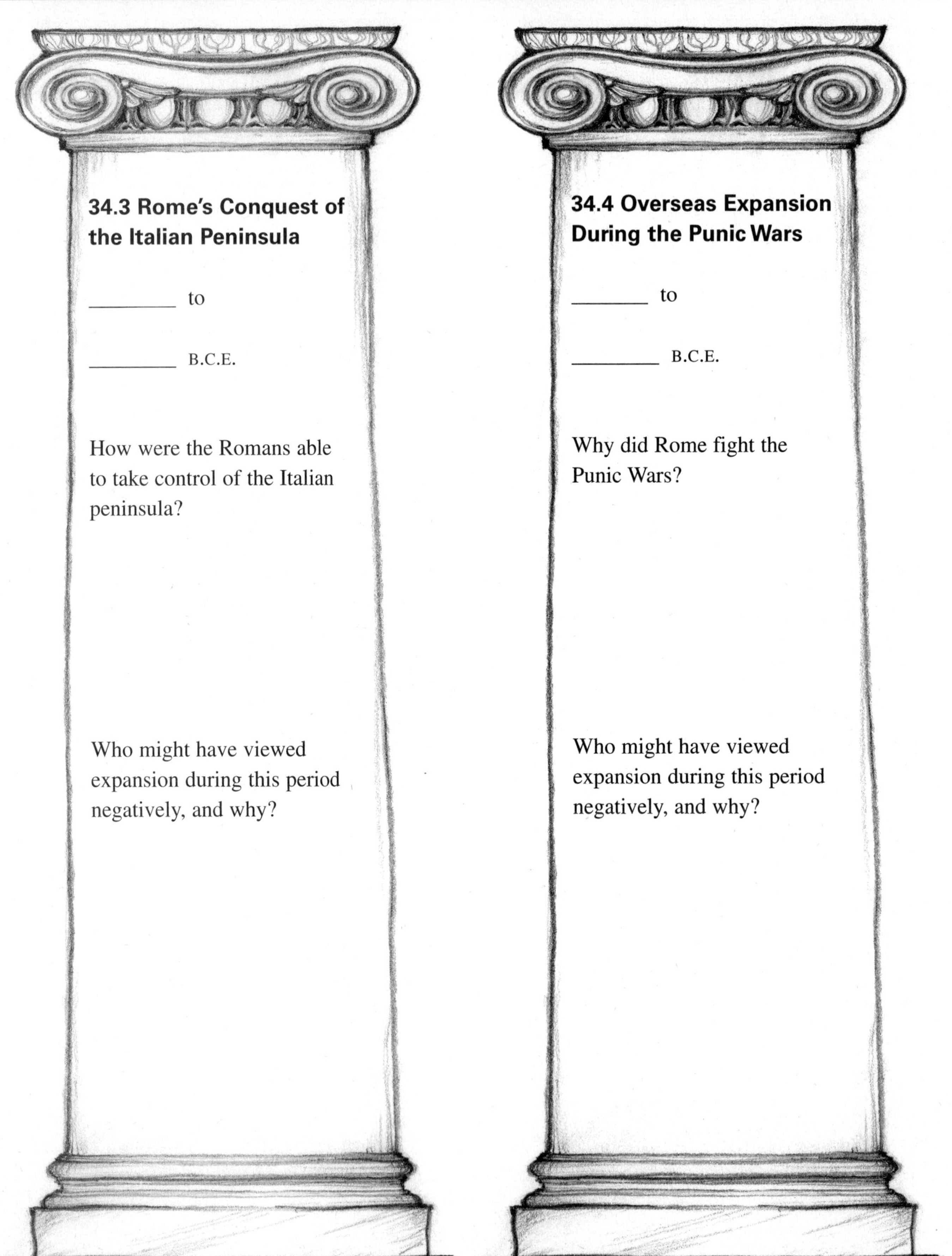

34.3 Rome's Conquest of the Italian Peninsula

________ to

________ B.C.E.

How were the Romans able to take control of the Italian peninsula?

Who might have viewed expansion during this period negatively, and why?

34.4 Overseas Expansion During the Punic Wars

________ to

________ B.C.E.

Why did Rome fight the Punic Wars?

Who might have viewed expansion during this period negatively, and why?

34.5 Expansion During the Final Years of the Republic

________ to

________ B.C.E.

When Julius Caesar became dictator of Rome, what reforms did he make?

Who might have viewed expansion during this period negatively, and why?

34.6 Rome Becomes an Empire

________ B.C.E. to

________ C.E.

What was the Pax Romana? Who established it?

Who might have viewed expansion during this period negatively, and why?

PROCESSING 34

Pretend you have been commissioned to write a poem praising the growth of the Roman Empire. Your poem should

- have a memorable title.
- contain six short stanzas, each one sentence in length.
- be written so that the first letters of the poem's stanzas spell out the word *EMPIRE*.
- include six of these terms: *Italian peninsula, Cincinnatus, Punic Wars, Hannibal, Gaul, Julius Caesar, dictator, Augustus, reforms*.
- incorporate vivid language, like that used in a eulogy (writing in praise of someone who has died).

The first line of your poem might look like this:

***E**mboldened by their defeat of the Etruscans, the mighty Romans confidently set out to bring the entire Italian peninsula under their control!*

PREVIEW 35

Make a sketch of an American teenager. Then add to your drawing at least five things an American teenager might need or want in daily life to be happy. Label each item, explaining what it is and why it is important.

READING NOTES 35

Find the box on pages 236–239 that corresponds to the section you read in *History Alive! The Ancient World.* Record the answer to the trivia question, and list three key differences between that aspect of life in ancient Rome and modern times. Then finish the drawing, and write a caption for it that describes what is happening.

35.3 Law and Order

1. Answer the trivia question.

2. List two key differences between ancient Rome and modern times.

3. Read the information at the station. Use it to complete the illustration and to write a caption for it.

35.4 Religion

1. Answer the trivia question.

2. List two key differences between ancient Rome and modern times.

3. Read the information at the station. Use it to complete the illustration and to write a caption for it.

35.5 Family Life

1. Answer the trivia question.

2. List three key differences between ancient Rome and modern times.

3. Read the information at the station. Use it to complete the illustration and to write a caption for it.

35.6 Food and Drink

1. Answer the trivia question.

2. List three key differences between ancient Rome and modern times.

3. Read the information at the station. Use it to complete the illustration and to write a caption for it.

35.7 Housing

1. Answer the trivia question.

2. List three key differences between ancient Rome and modern times.

3. Read the information at the station. Use it to complete the illustration and to write a caption for it.

35.8 Education

1. Answer the trivia question.

2 List three key differences between ancient Rome and modern times.

3. Read the information at the station. Use it to complete the illustration and to write a caption for it.

35.9 Recreation

1. Answer the trivia question.

2. List three key differences between ancient Rome and modern times.

3. Read the information at the station. Use it to complete the illustration and to write a caption for it.

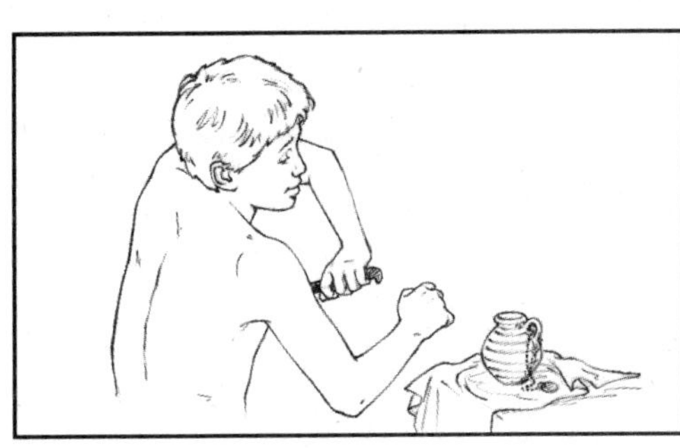

35.10 Country Life

1. Answer the trivia question.

2. List three key differences between ancient Rome and modern times.

3. Read the information at the station. Use it to complete the illustration and to write a caption for it.

PROCESSING 35

Make a sketch of a Roman teenager. Then add to your drawing at least five things a Roman teenager might need or want in daily life to be happy. Label each item, explaining what it is and why it is important.

PREVIEW 36

In the space below, explain how a belief or an idea is like a seed. What does it need to grow? What things might prevent it from growing?

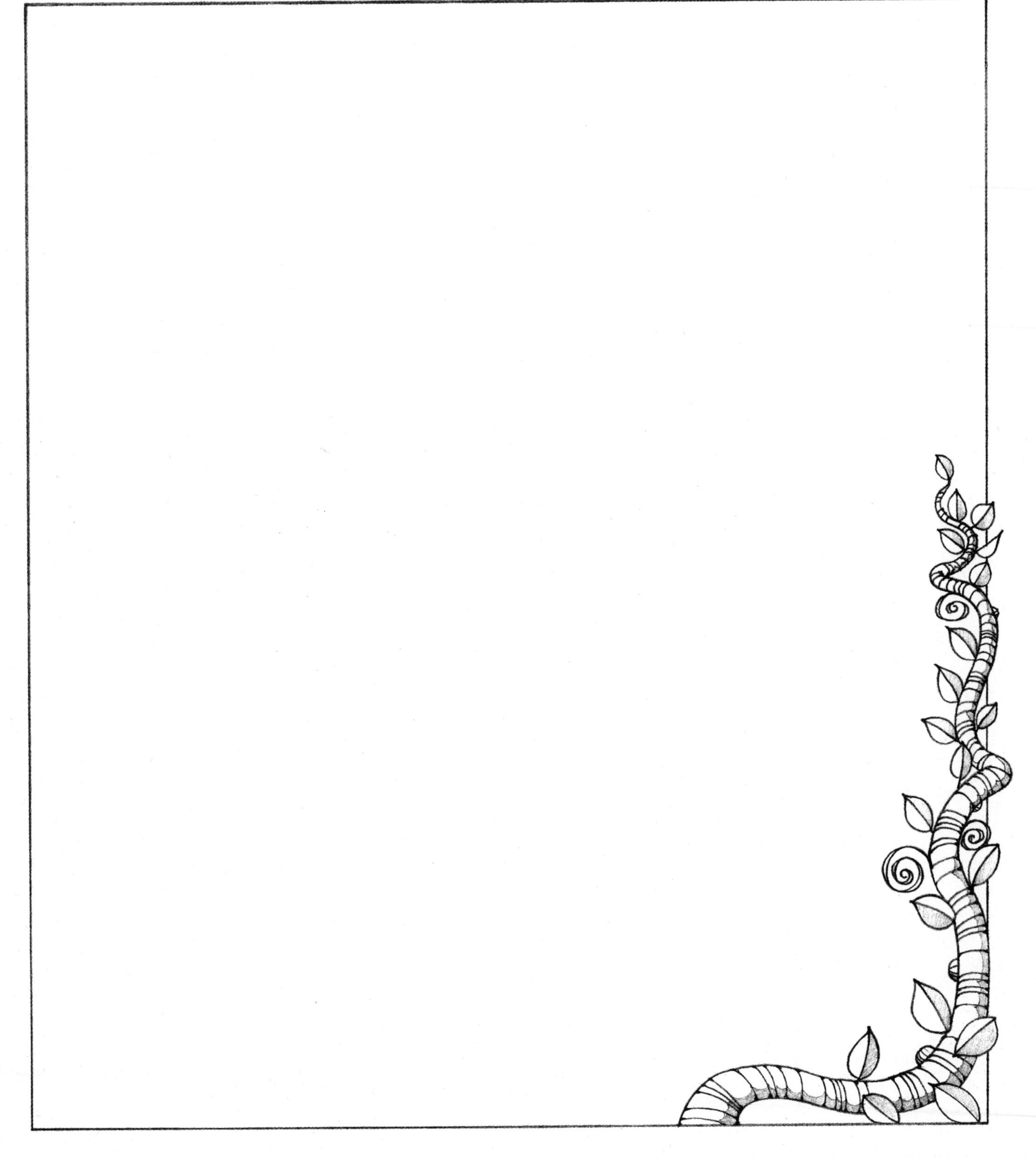

READING NOTES 36

Read Sections 36.2 and 36.3 in *History Alive! The Ancient World* and take notes below.

36.2 Judea: The Birthplace of Christianity

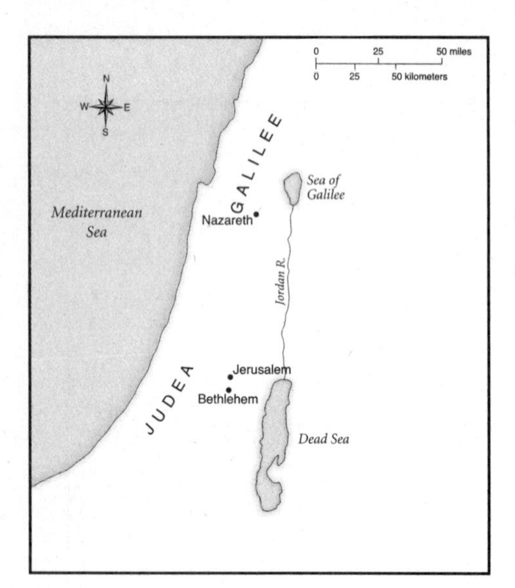

Why was there unrest in Judea after it came under Roman rule?

How did the Roman prefect rule Judea?

36.3 Writings About the Life of Jesus

What are the gospels?

Who wrote the gospels, and when did they write them?

For Sections 36.4–36.8, follow these steps:

1. Carefully examine the artwork on pages 243–245 and read the biblical passages your teacher gave you to determine which passage matches each work of art.
2. After your teacher has revealed the correct passage, glue the passage in the appropriate box on pages 243–245.
3. Read that section of the chapter, and answer the related questions.
4. Underline key words and phrases in the passage. Draw lines connecting them to visual details in the artwork.

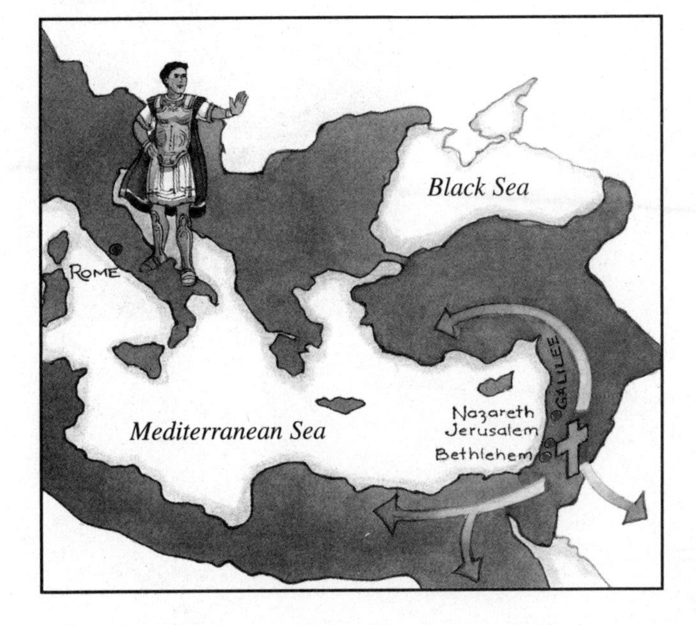

36.4 The Birth of Jesus

According to the gospels, where was Jesus born?

What did Jesus study and learn about as a child?

Why was Jesus' baptism a turning point in his life?

READING NOTES 36

36.5 Jesus' Teaching

According to the gospels, what did Jesus say were the most important of all the Jewish laws?

Why did Jesus' teachings upset some people?

36.6 The Crucifixion and Resurrection

According to the gospels, why was Jesus condemned to die on a cross?

Why was belief in Jesus' resurrection so important to his disciples and other followers?

36.7 The Missionary Work of Paul

What caused Saul to stop persecuting Christians and become a missionary?

How did Paul's work help spread Christianity?

36.8 Persecution and Triumph

Why were Christians considered a threat to Rome?

How did Rome's persecution of Christians help Christianity grow and spread?

PROCESSING 36

Follow these steps to analyze your leftover biblical passage:

1. Glue the passage in the box below. Read it carefully, and draw a picture to illustrate it.

Illustration of This Passage

2. Complete the sentences below to compare what you learned about the growth of Christianity with the growth of a seed. The first sentence has been completed for you.

The small seed is like *Jesus' teachings*.

The person who planted the seed is like ____________________.

The water that helps the seed to grow is like ____________________.

The large plant that grows from the seed is like ____________________.

The birds that nest in the plant are like ____________________.

3. Now label the parts of your drawing above to show how Christianity began and what helped it to grow and spread. For example, you might label a seed under the ground *Jesus' teachings*.

PREVIEW 37

Do you agree or disagree with the statement below? Write your ideas between the pillars. Give examples to support your opinion.

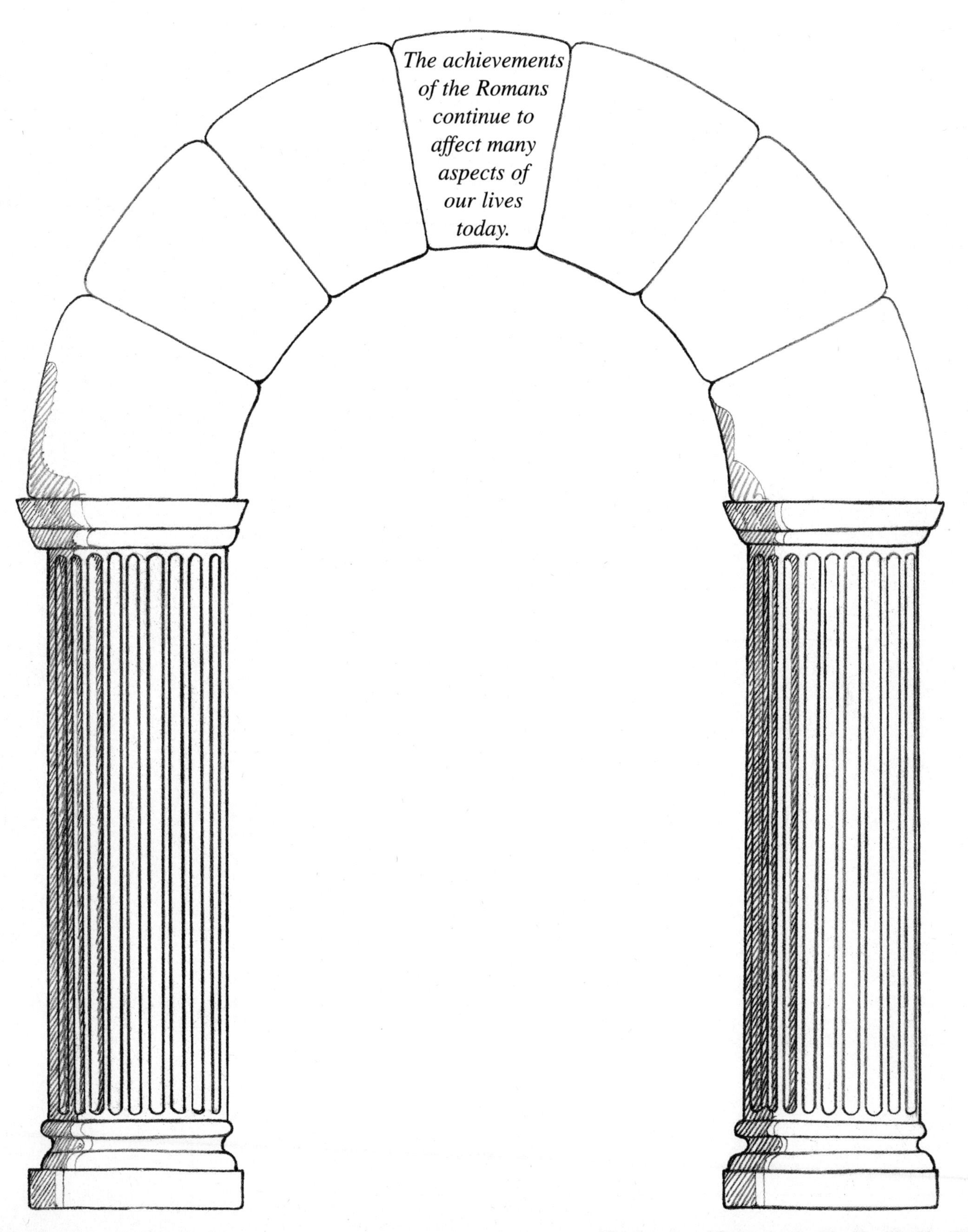

READING NOTES 37

After reading each of Sections 37.3–37.6 in *History Alive! The Ancient World,* answer the corresponding questions.

37.3 Art
What important art forms did the ancient Romans develop?   What are some examples of Roman art forms that influence modern life?

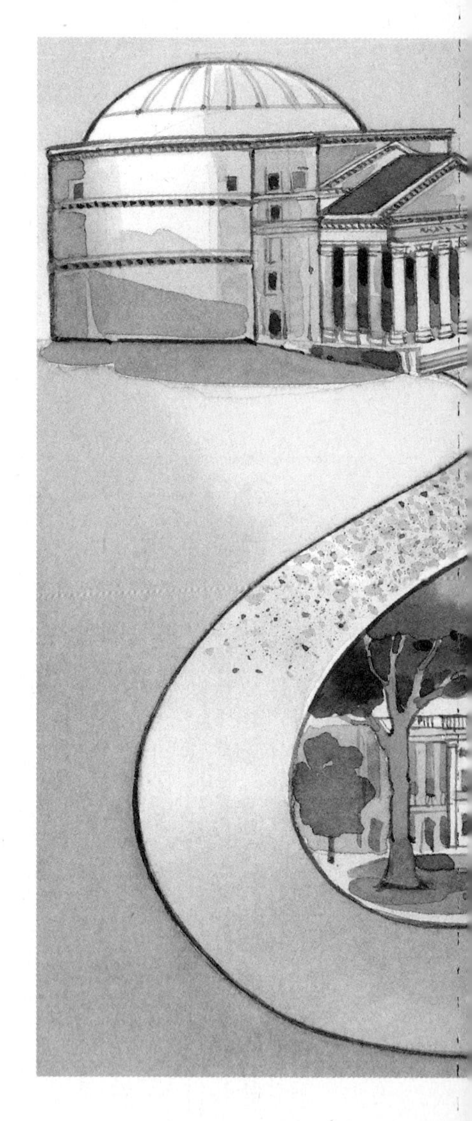

37.4 Architecture and Engineering
What were some important architectural and engineering achievements of the ancient Romans?   What are some examples of Roman architecture and engineering that influence modern life?

37.5 Language

How was the Latin alphabet of Rome different from the English alphabet?

What Roman numerals are used for the numbers 1 through 10? How were the numbers 50, 100, 500, and 1,000 written by the Romans?

What are some examples of Roman language that influence modern life?

37.6 Philosophy and Law

What were the most important ideas in Roman philosophy and law?

What are some examples of ways Roman philosophy and law have affected modern life?

PROCESSING 37

Find three examples of Roman cultural influences in your community. For example, you might see a building with a dome, a mosaic, or a sign containing a word derived from Latin.

Sketch or take a photograph of each example. Then write a caption for each example. In the caption, describe the example, state where it is located in your community, and explain the Roman cultural influences it contains.

TIMELINE CHALLENGE 6

Use the timeline below to help you complete Items A–F. When completed, each item should include the following:

- the date(s) and a short written description of the item.
- a simple symbol or drawing to represent the item.
- an appropriate geometric shape surrounding the symbol or drawing. The shapes correspond to the categories listed above the right side of the timeline.
- a color bar or dot in the appropriate location on the timeline.
- a line connecting the bar or dot to the geometric shape.

B. 31 B.C.E.
Augustus Caesar becomes the first emperor of Rome.

A. 616 – 509 B.C.E.
Two main classes of Roman society, ____________________ and ____________________, develop under Etruscan rule.

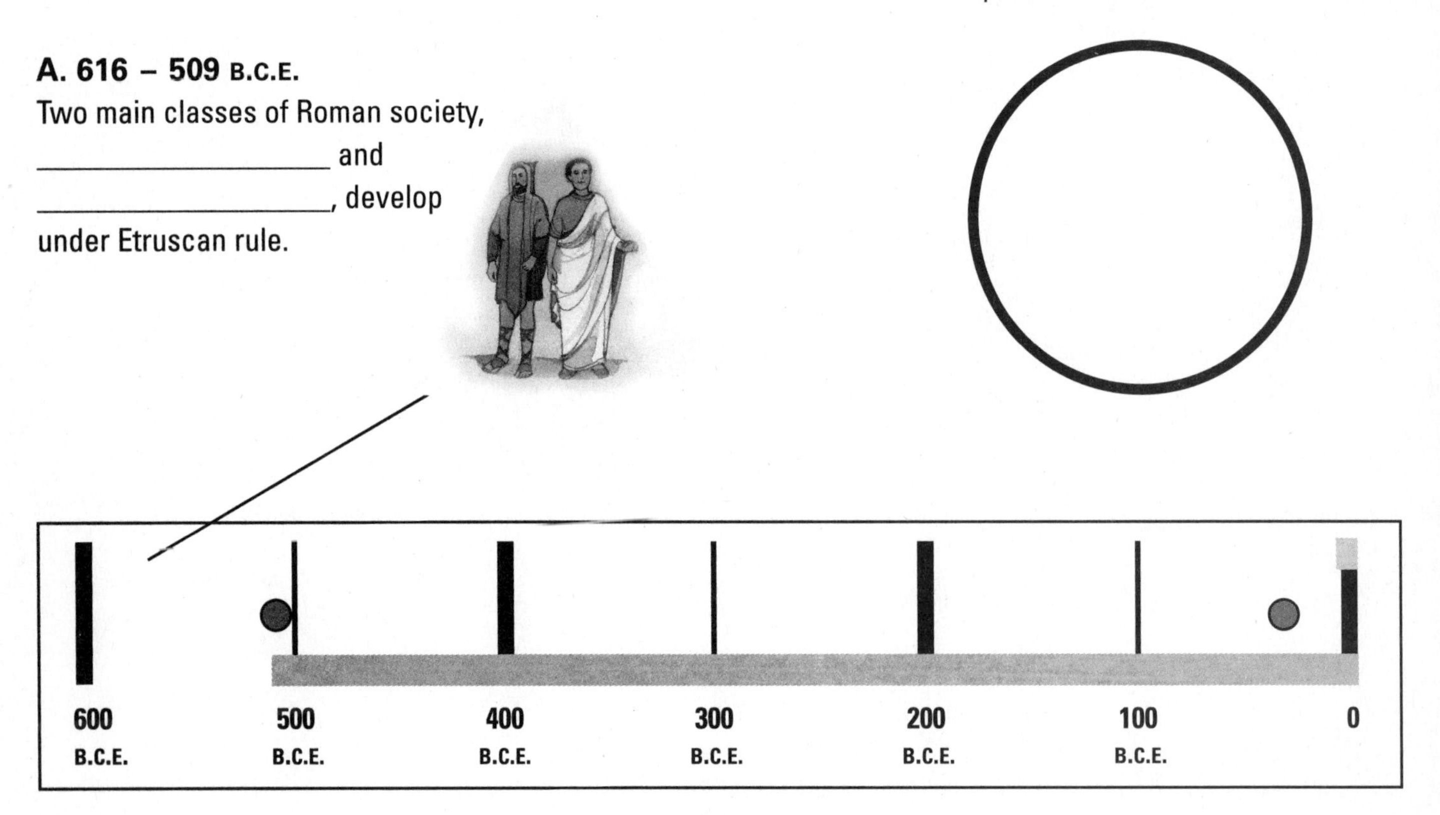

D. 509 B.C.E.
The Roman Republic is created, giving political rights to patricians but not plebeians.

△ Social Structure ◯ Government □ Religion ⬠ Arts ⯃ Technology ▱ Writing System

C. About 118 – 128 C.E.
The Pantheon, with its huge dome, is built.

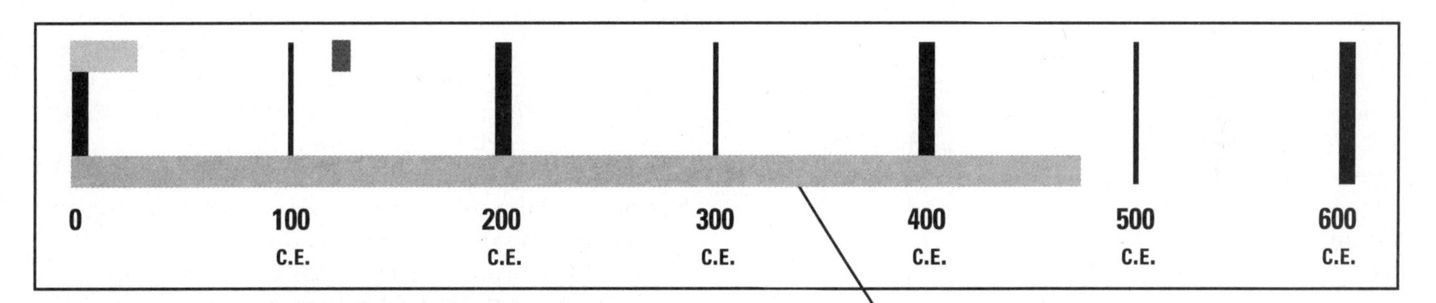

E. About 6 B.C.E. – 27 C.E.
The life and teachings of ______________ lay the foundation of Christianity.

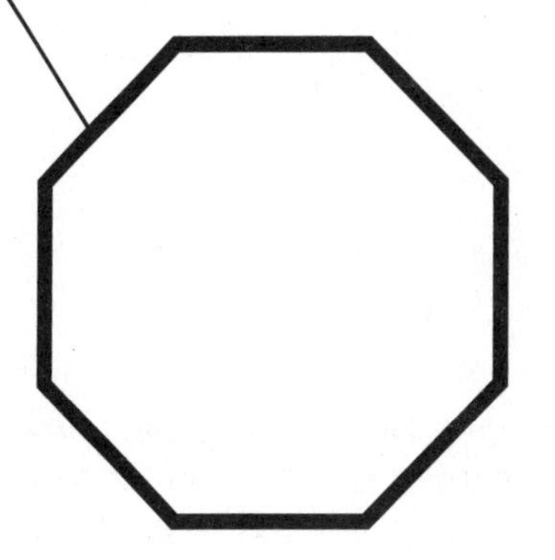

F. ____________________
The Romans build 53,000 miles of roads to connect their republic and, later, empire.

Credits

Lesson 1
pp. 10–11: Doug Roy.

Lesson 2
p. 14, upper: Susan Jaekel. **p. 14, lower**: Doug Roy. **p. 15, upper**: Susan Jaekel. **p. 15, lower**: Doug Roy. **p. 16, upper**: Susan Jaekel. **p. 16, lower**: Doug Roy. **p. 17, upper**: Susan Jaekel. **p. 17, lower**: Doug Roy. **p. 18, upper**: Susan Jaekel. **p. 18, lower**: Doug Roy.

Lesson 3
pp. 22–26: Doug Roy.

Lesson 4
pp. 28–29: Doug Roy.

Lesson 5
p. 31: Doug Roy. **p. 33**: Doug Roy. **p. 34**: Doug Roy. **p. 36**: Doug Roy.

Lesson 6
p. 39: Susan Jaekel. **pp. 40–43**: Susan Jaekel. **p. 47**: Len Ebert.

Lesson 8
p. 59: DJ Simison. **p. 60**: Susan Jaekel, Doug Roy. **pp. 61–63**: Doug Roy. **p. 64**: Susan Jaekel.

Lesson 9
p. 69: DJ Simison.

Lesson 10
pp. 72–75: Len Ebert. **p. 76, left**: Doug Roy. **p. 76, right**: Len Ebert.

Lesson 11
p. 77: Susan Jaekel. **pp. 78–80**: Doug Roy.

Lesson 12
pp. 86–87: Len Ebert.

Lesson 13
p. 95: Doug Roy. **p. 96**: Doug Roy.

Lesson 14
p. 97: Stoneware bangle (contemporary); © Harappa Bazzar. **p. 98, upper**: Doug Roy. **p. 98, lower**: Doug Roy. **pp. 98–99, center**: Renate Lohmann. **p. 99, upper**: Doug Roy. **p. 99, lower**: Doug Roy. **p. 100, upper**: Doug Roy. **p. 100, lower**: Doug Roy. **pp. 100–101, center**: Renate Lohmann. **p. 101, upper**: Doug Roy. **p. 101, lower**: Doug Roy. **p. 102**: Doug Roy.

Lesson 15
p. 104: Susan Jaekel.

Lesson 16
p. 107: Susan Jaekel. **pp. 108–110**: Len Ebert. **p. 111**: Len Ebert. **p. 112**: Len Ebert.

Lesson 17
p. 113: Doug Roy. **pp. 114–115**: Renate Lohmann. **p. 118**: Doug Roy.

Lesson 18
p. 119: Doug Roy. **pp. 120–123**: Doug Roy. **pp. 124–125**: Len Ebert.

Lesson 19
p. 134: Susan Jaekel.

Lesson 20
p. 135: Susan Jaekel. **pp. 136–137**: Len Ebert. **p. 138**: Doug Roy.

Lesson 21
pp. 140–142: Len Ebert.

Lesson 22
p. 145, upper: *Battle at Wu Yan,* Red-Eyebrow uprising, peasants fighting Han army, 22 C.E., Wu Yan battlefield, present-day Dong Pin County, Shandong Province, China; © Liu Liqun/ChinaStock. **p. 145, lower:** Susan Jaekel. **p. 146, upper left:** *Promenade of Qin Shi Huang Di* (Tsin dynasty emperor (221–206 B.C.E.)), from *The Lives of the Emperors of China,* Qing dynasty, 17th C., watercolor on silk; Bibliothèque Nationale, Paris, France; © Giraudon/Art Resource, NY. **p. 146, upper center upper**: Bronze coin of Emperor Ch'in Shi-Huang-ti, 220 B.C.E.; Ronald Sheridan Ancient Art & Architecture Collection. **p. 146, upper center lower:** Bronze bowl-shaped oval measure, 221–207 B.C.E.; © ChinaStock. **p. 146, upper right upper:** Bronze standardized weight, 221–207 B.C.E.; © China Stock. **p. 146, upper right lower:** *The Art of War (Sun Zi Bin Fa),* written on bamboo strips found in Shan-dong/Han dynasty tomb; © ChinaStock. **p. 146, lower:** Susan Jaekel. **p. 147, upper:** *Building the Great Wall,* © Hsien-Min Yang/National Geographic Image Collection. **p. 147, lower:** Susan Jaekel. **p. 148, upper:** *Killing of the Confucian Scholars by Order of Emperor Qin Shi Huang Ti,* Qin dynasty, 221–206 B.C.E.; Sovfoto/Eastfoto/New China Pictures. **p. 148, lower:** Susan Jaekel. **p. 149, upper:** *Building Emperor Ch'in Shih Huang Ti's Tomb;* © Hsien-Min Yang/National Geographic Image Collection. **p. 149, lower:** Susan Jaekel.

Lesson 23
p. 151: Doug Roy. **pp. 152–155:** Doug Roy. **p. 156:** Doug Roy.

Lesson 24
pp. 158–159: Doug Roy. **pp. 160–161:** Doug Roy. **pp. 162–163:** Len Ebert.

Lesson 25
p. 168: Doug Roy. **p. 170:** Doug Roy.

Lesson 26
pp. 172–173: Len Ebert. **p. 174:** Doug Roy.

Lesson 27
pp. 176–179: Renate Lohmann. **p. 180:** Doug Roy.

Lesson 28
p. 181: Doug Roy. **p. 182, upper:** Doug Roy. **p. 182, lower:** Len Ebert. **p. 183, upper:** Doug Roy. **p. 183, lower:** Len Ebert. **p. 184, upper:** Doug Roy. **p. 184, lower:** Len Ebert. **p. 185, upper:** Doug Roy. **p. 185, lower:** Len Ebert. **p. 186, upper:** Doug Roy. **p. 186, lower:** Len Ebert. **p. 187:** Doug Roy.

Lesson 29
p. 190: Doug Roy. **p. 191:** Renate Lohmann.

Lesson 30
p. 196: Susan Jaekel. **p. 198:** Susan Jaekel. **p. 200:** Susan Jaekel. **p. 202:** Susan Jaekel. **p. 204:** Doug Roy.

Lesson 31
p. 205: Susan Jaekel. **pp. 206–211:** Doug Roy. **p. 212:** DJ Simison. **pp. 214–215:** Len Ebert.

Lesson 32
p. 221, upper left: Len Ebert. **p. 221, upper right:** Circus Maximus, Rome; North Wind Picture Archives. **p. 221, lower left:** Len Ebert. **p. 221, lower right:** Circus Maximus, Rome; North Wind Picture Archives. **p. 222, upper left:** Len Ebert. **p. 222, upper right:** Street near Temple of Fortuna Augusta, Pompeii, Italy; © Bettmann/Corbis. **p. 222, lower left:** Len Ebert. **p. 222, lower right:** Street near Temple of Fortuna Augusta, Pompeii, Italy; © Bettmann/Corbis. **p. 223, upper left:** Len Ebert. **p. 223, upper right:** Forum of ancient Rome; North Wind Picture Archives. **p. 223, lower left:** Len Ebert. **p. 223, lower right:** Forum of ancient Rome; North Wind Picture Archives. **p. 224:** Doug Roy.

Lesson 33
pp. 226–227: Susan Jaekel.

Lesson 34
p. 229: Doug Roy. **pp. 232–233:** Renate Lohmann. **p. 234:** Doug Roy.

Lesson 35
p. 236, upper: Susan Jaekel. **p. 236, lower:** Susan Jaekel. **pp. 236–237, center:** Doug Roy. **p. 237, upper:** Susan Jaekel. **p. 237, lower:** DJ Simison. **p. 238, upper:** DJ Simison. **p. 238, lower:** DJ Simison. **pp. 238–239, center:** Doug Roy. **p. 239, upper:** DJ Simison. **p. 239, lower:** Susan Jaekel.

Lesson 36
p. 241: Doug Roy. **p. 242, lower:** First page of a religious codex made for the 73rd Jacobite patriarch Michael son of Zaraa (detail). Egypt, Damietta, Mamluk dynasty, 1175–1200. Gold and color on parchment; 35.6 x 22.8 cm. © Freer Gallery of Art, Smithsonian Institution, Washington, D.C.: Purchase, F1955.11. **p. 243, upper:** Len Ebert. **p. 243, lower:** Nativity, colored engraving after Gustave Doré; The Granger Collection, New York. **p. 244, upper:** Sermon on the Mount, colored engraving after Gustave Doré; The Granger Collection, New York. **p. 244, lower:** *The Crucifixion,* 1457–1460, Andrea Mantegna, oil on panel; The Granger Collection, New York. **p. 245, upper:** Paul in prison, writing the Epistles; North Wind Picture Archives. **p. 245, lower:** Christian martyrs in Colosseum, ancient Rome; North Wind Picture Archives.

Lesson 37
p. 247: Len Ebert. **pp. 248–249:** Len Ebert. **pp. 252– 253:** Len Ebert.